Level B

MATHEMATICS

Skills, Concepts, Problem Solving

Author: Albert E. Filano

Editor: K. E. Possler

Illustrators: Jim Machin and Harry Norcross

Cover Illustrator: Cary Michael Trout

ISBN 0-8454-0172-6

Continental Press

Elizabethtown, PA 17022

Contents

1
one

Circle each set of 1.   Circle 1 object in each set.

one

two

Circle each set of **2**.

Circle **2** objects in each set.

Circle each set of **3**.

Circle **3** objects in each set.

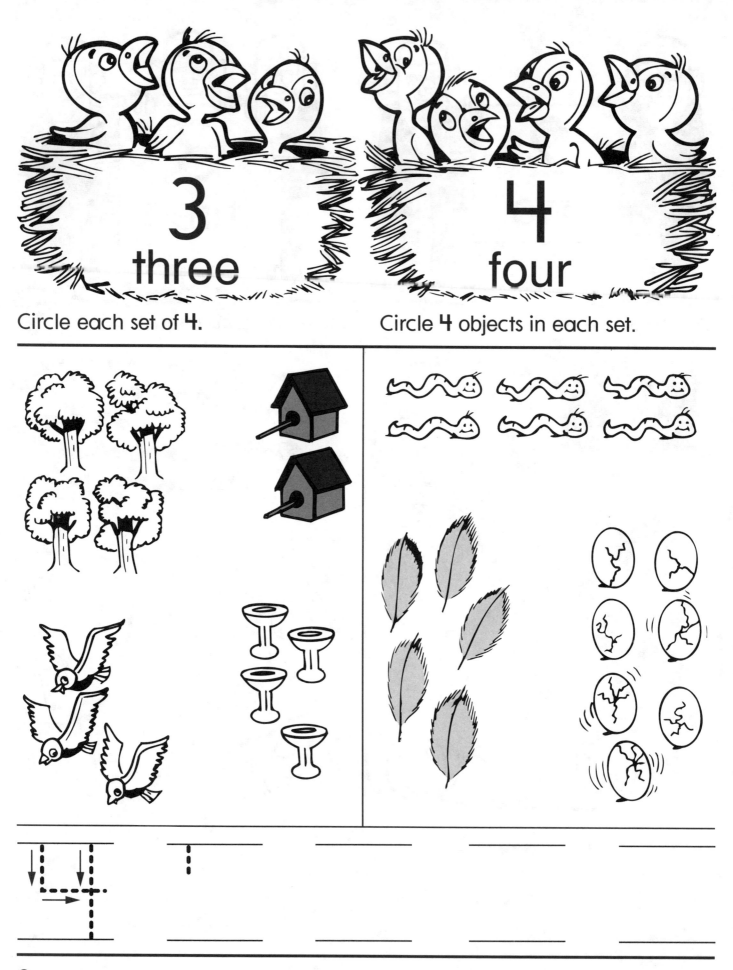

3 three

4 four

Circle each set of 4.

Circle 4 objects in each set.

The Number 4

4 four

Circle each set of **5.**

5 five

Circle **5** objects in each set.

2 two   1 one   0 zero

Mark each set of **0**.

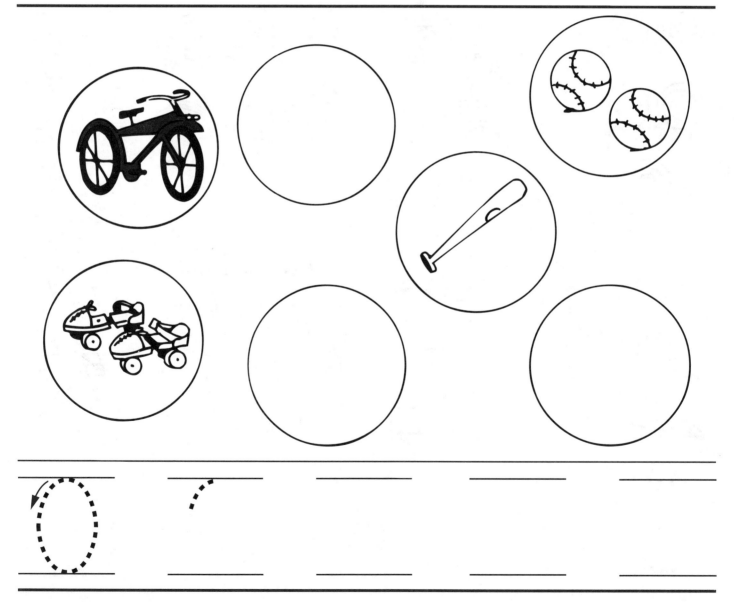

Write the number of people in each boat.

5

3

0

2

1

4

Match the numbers with the spots on the fish.

Write the numbers in order.

Connect the dots in order.

Start

Look at the picture.

Write how many.

2 _____   4 _____   1 _____

5 _____   0 _____   3 _____

Circle each set of **6**.

Circle **6** objects in each set.

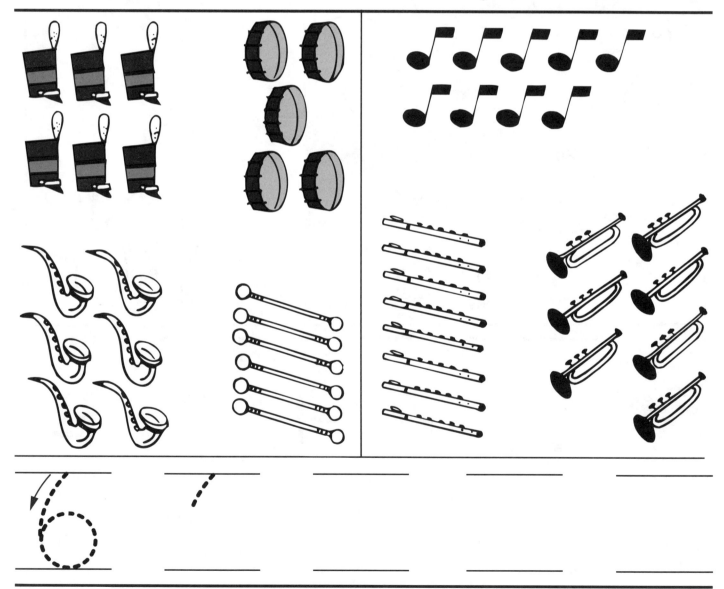

The Number 6

6 six

7 seven

Circle each set of **7**.

Circle **7** objects in each set.

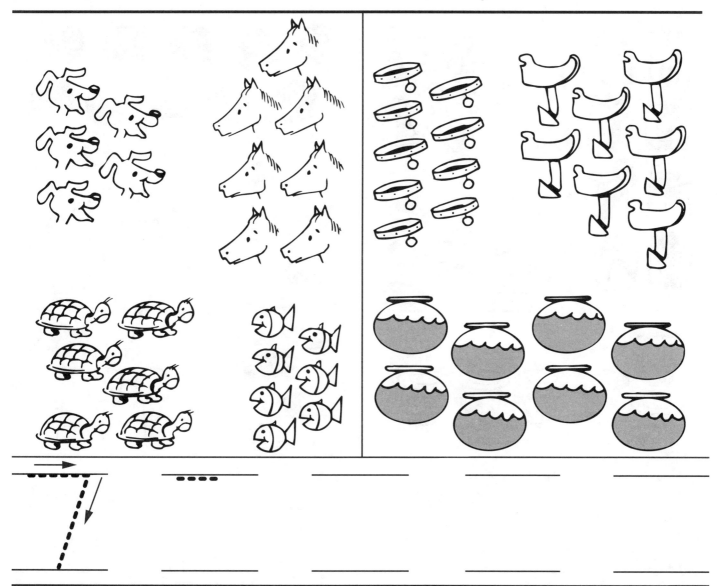

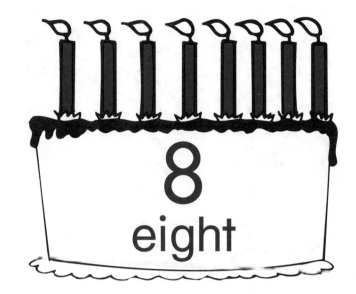

Circle each set of **8**.

Circle **8** objects in each set.

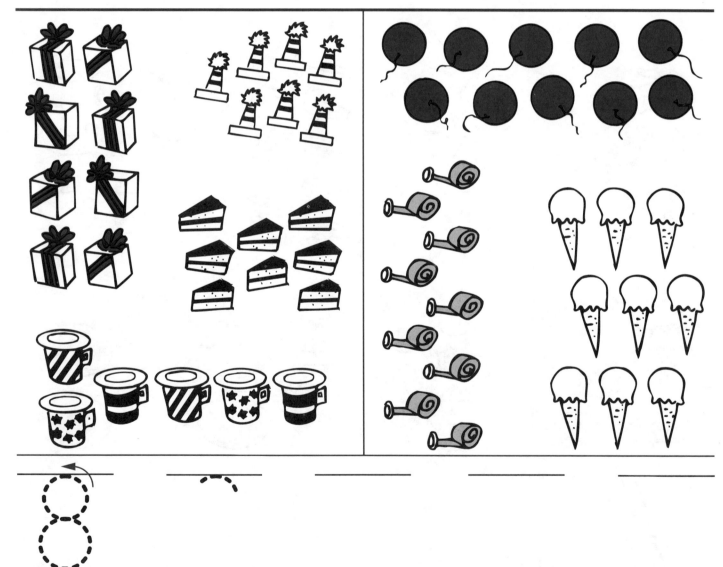

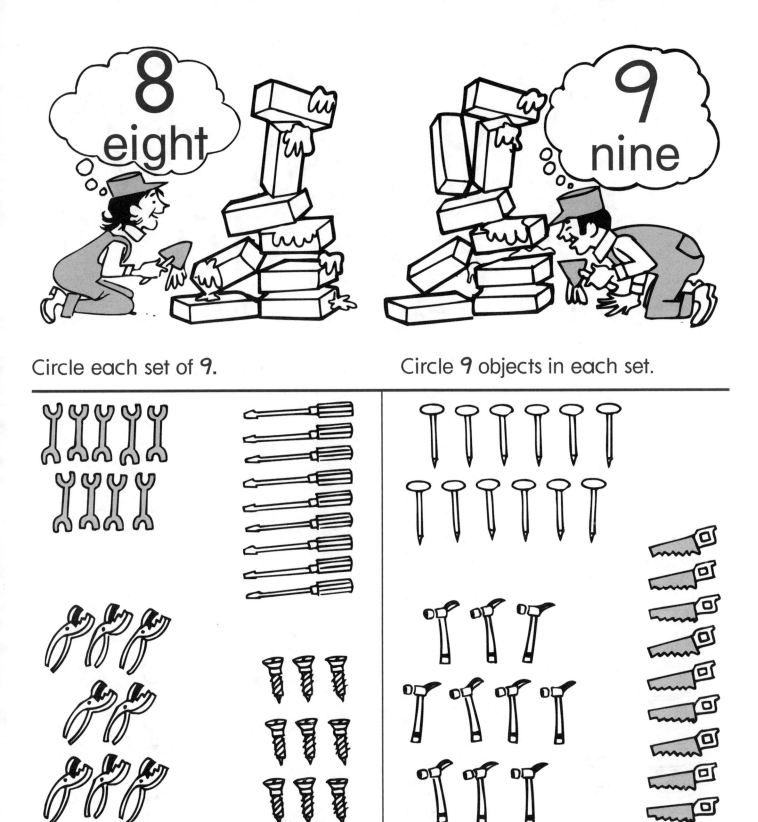

Circle each set of 9.

Circle 9 objects in each set.

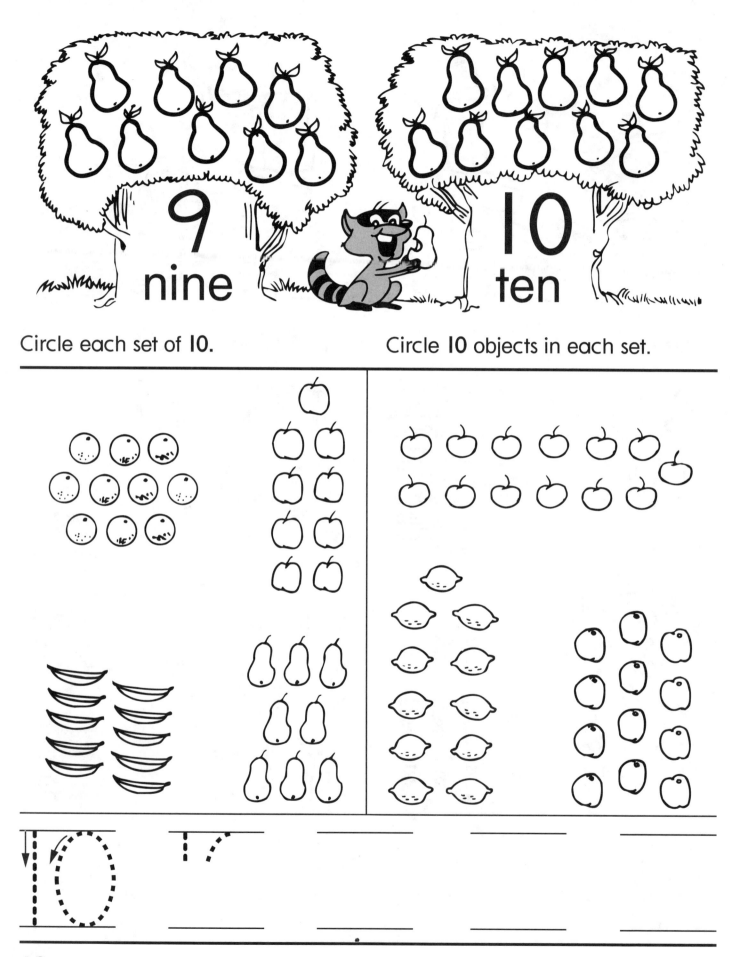

9 nine

10 ten

Circle each set of **10**.

Circle **10** objects in each set.

The Number 10

Circle the correct number for each set.

8   10   7

10   9   6

7   9   6

6   7   9

7   6   10

7   8   10

8   6   9

Write the number that tells how many.

Color the correct number of objects in each row.

6

7

8

9

10

Write the missing numbers.

6 _____ _____

9 _____

Order of Numbers 6–10

Match.

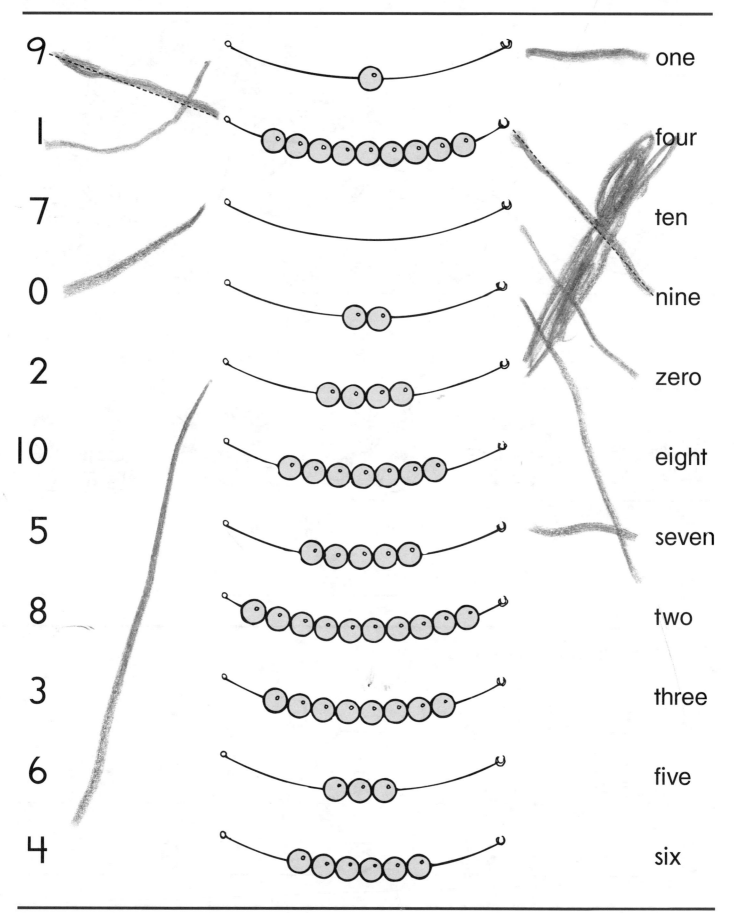

9

1

7

0

2

10

5

8

3

6

4

one

four

ten

nine

zero

eight

seven

two

three

five

six

Write the numbers from 0 to 10 in order.

Write the missing numbers.

0 __1__ 2 __ 4 __ 6 __ 8 __ 10

__ 1 __ 3 __ 5 __ 7 __ 9 __

0 __ __ 3 __ 5 __ __ 8 __ __

Color the boxes to show how many.

10						
9						
8						
7						
6						
5						
4						
3						
2						
1						
	🌭	🥤	🐜	🍔	🧁	🍴

Match one to one.

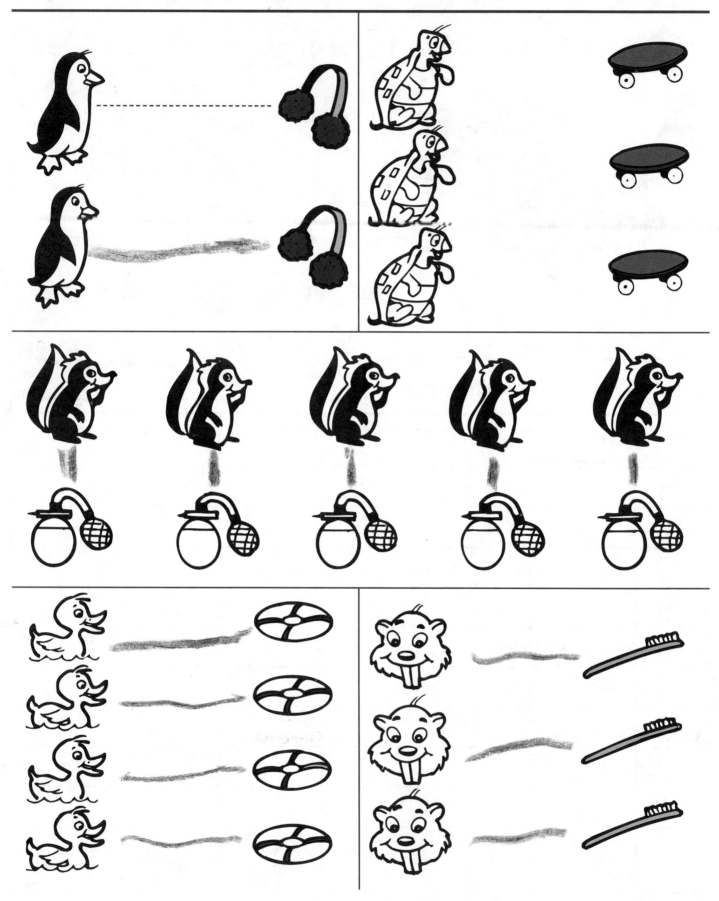

Matching Sets: Same Number

Match as many as you can. Circle the set with **more**.

Match as many as you can. Circle the set with **less.**

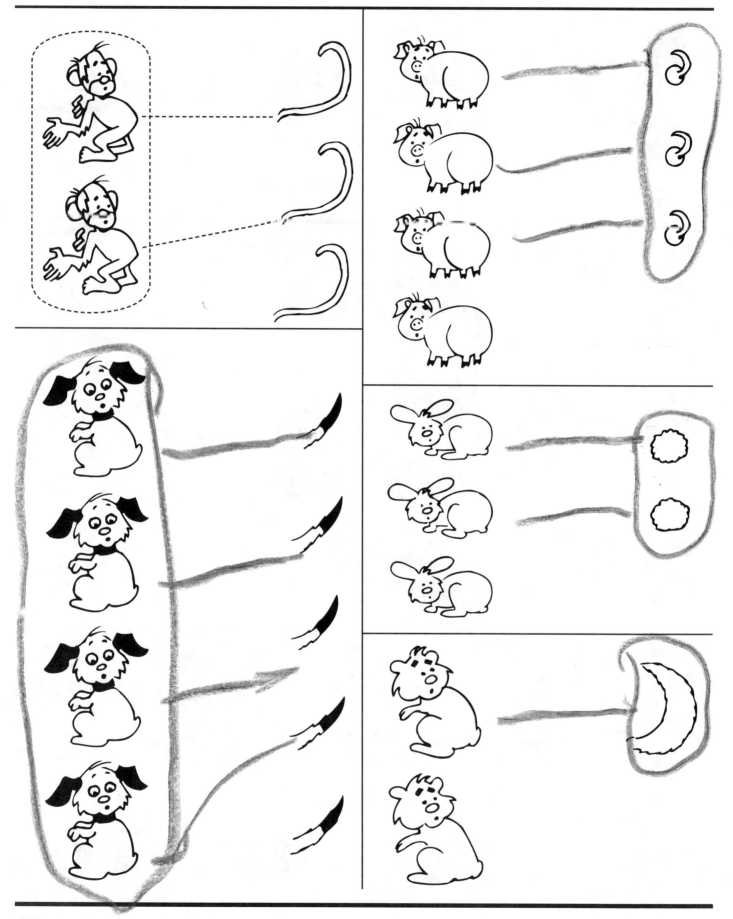

 **3** is greater than **2**

Circle the set with **more.**
Then write the numbers that make the sentence true.

___8___ is greater than ___5___   ___6___ is greater than ___3___

___9___ is greater than ___4___   ___10___ is greater than ___7___

___1___ is greater than ___0___   ____ is greater than ____

___5___ is greater than ___2___   ____ is greater than ____

___7___ is greater than ___6___   ____ is greater than ____

3 is less than 4

Circle the set with **less.**
Then write the numbers that make the sentence true.

_5_ is less than _7_

____ is less than ____

____ is less than ____

____ is less than ____

____ is less than ____

____ is less than ____

____ is less than ____

____ is less than ____

____ is less than ____

____ is less than ____

Comparing Numbers: Less Than

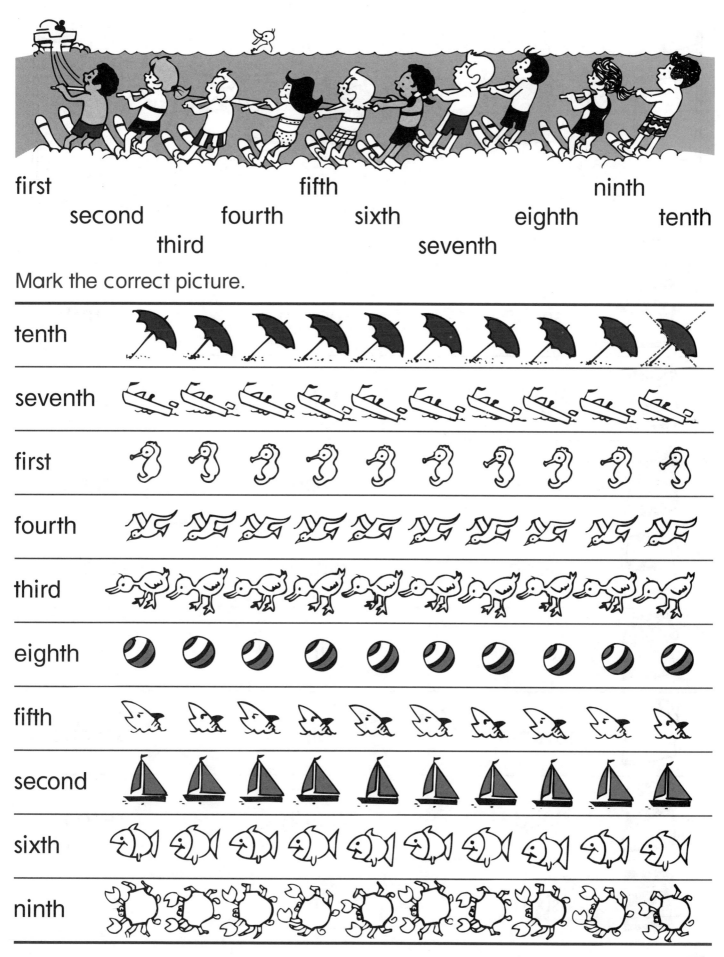

first

second

third

fourth

fifth

sixth

seventh

eighth

ninth

tenth

Mark the correct picture.

tenth

seventh

first

fourth

third

eighth

fifth

second

sixth

ninth

Mark the correct answer.

	sixth	~~second~~	fourth
	eighth	third	fifth
	third	sixth	fifth
	fourth	eighth	seventh
	tenth	first	fourth
	seventh	third	second
	third	fourth	second
	sixth	fifth	eighth

Ordinal Numbers

2 plus 1 equals 3

2 + 1 = 3

Add.

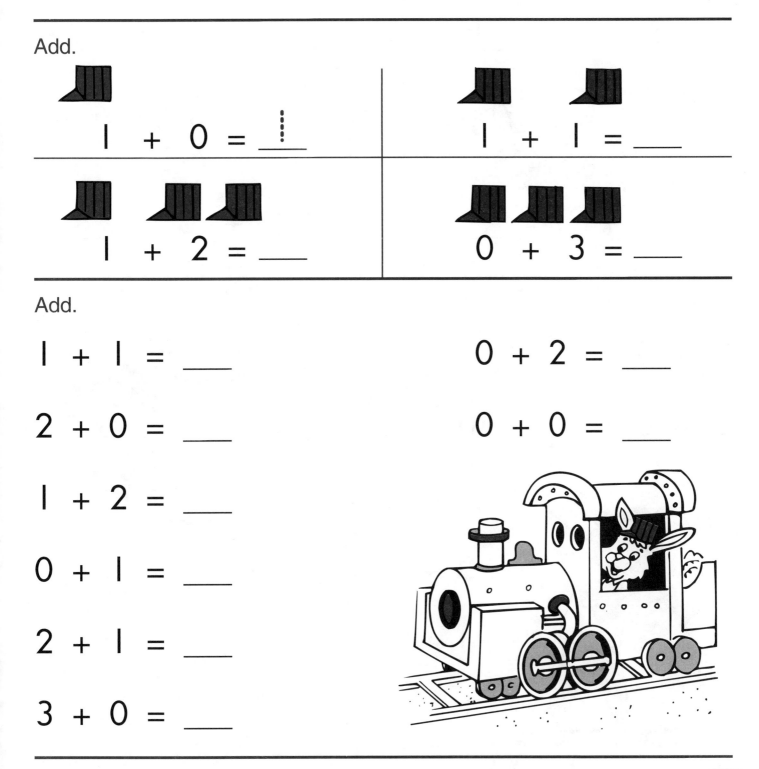

1 + 0 = 1

1 + 1 = ___

1 + 2 = ___

0 + 3 = ___

Add.

1 + 1 = ___

0 + 2 = ___

2 + 0 = ___

0 + 0 = ___

1 + 2 = ___

0 + 1 = ___

2 + 1 = ___

3 + 0 = ___

Add.

$$3 + 1 = \underline{4}$$

$$2 + 2 = \underline{}$$

$$0 + 4 = \underline{}$$

$$1 + 3 = \underline{}$$

Add.

$$4 + 0 = \underline{}$$

$$2 + 2 = \underline{}$$

$$2 + 1 = \underline{}$$

$$0 + 2 = \underline{}$$

$$1 + 2 = \underline{}$$

$$0 + 4 = \underline{}$$

$$3 + 1 = \underline{}$$

$$3 + 0 = \underline{}$$

$$1 + 1 = \underline{}$$

$$1 + 3 = \underline{}$$

Addition : Facts for 4

Add.

4 + 1 = _5_

3 + 2 = ___

2 + 3 = ___

0 + 5 = ___

Add.

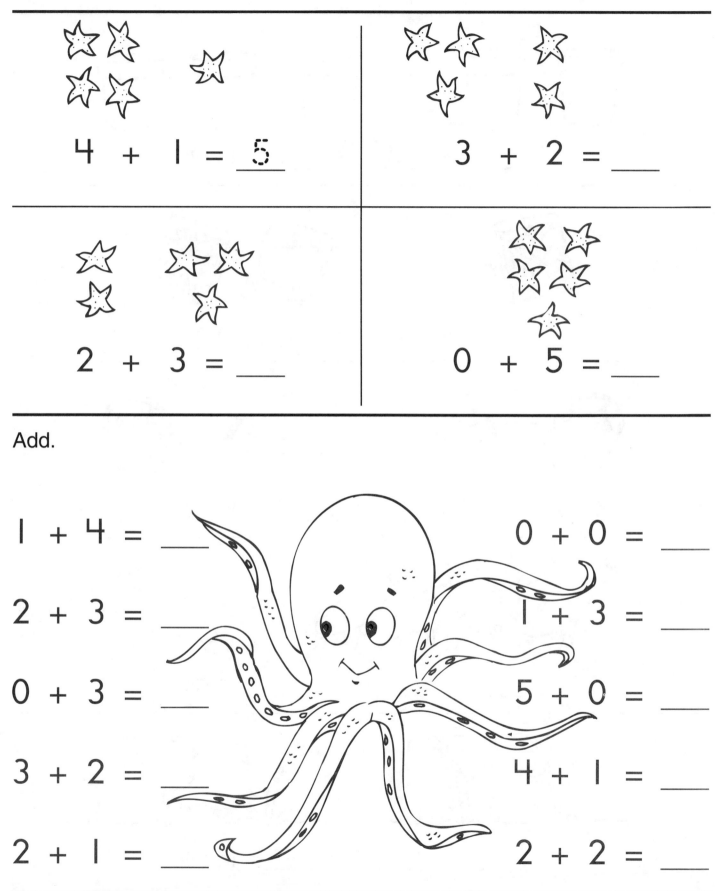

1 + 4 = ___

2 + 3 = ___

0 + 3 = ___

3 + 2 = ___

2 + 1 = ___

0 + 0 = ___

1 + 3 = ___

5 + 0 = ___

4 + 1 = ___

2 + 2 = ___

Write addition sentences to find how many in all.

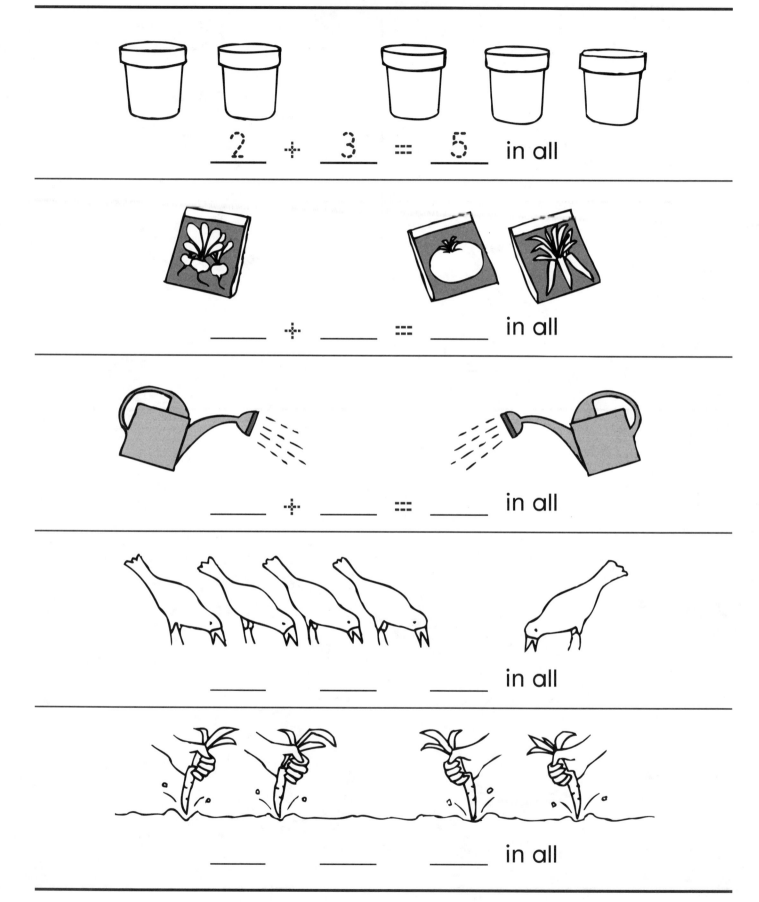

_2_ + _3_ = _5_ in all

___ + ___ = ___ in all

___ + ___ = ___ in all

___ ___ ___ in all

___ ___ ___ in all

Problem Solving: Writing Addition Sentences

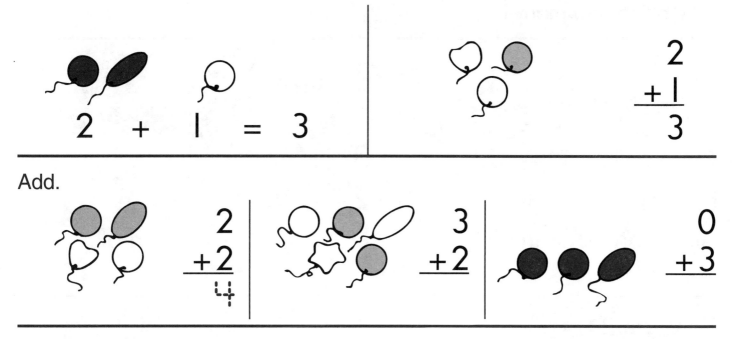

$$2 + 1 = 3$$

$$\begin{array}{r} 2 \\ +1 \\ \hline 3 \end{array}$$

Add.

$$\begin{array}{r} 2 \\ +2 \\ \hline 4 \end{array}$$

$$\begin{array}{r} 3 \\ +2 \\ \hline \end{array}$$

$$\begin{array}{r} 0 \\ +3 \\ \hline \end{array}$$

Add.

$$\begin{array}{r} 4 \\ +1 \\ \hline \end{array}$$

$$\begin{array}{r} 1 \\ +2 \\ \hline \end{array}$$

$$\begin{array}{r} 2 \\ +0 \\ \hline \end{array}$$

$$\begin{array}{r} 1 \\ +1 \\ \hline \end{array}$$

$$\begin{array}{r} 1 \\ +4 \\ \hline \end{array}$$

$$\begin{array}{r} 0 \\ +5 \\ \hline \end{array}$$

$$\begin{array}{r} 3 \\ +1 \\ \hline \end{array}$$

$$\begin{array}{r} 2 \\ +3 \\ \hline \end{array}$$

$$\begin{array}{r} 2 \\ +1 \\ \hline \end{array}$$

$$\begin{array}{r} 0 \\ +0 \\ \hline \end{array}$$

Add to find how many in all.

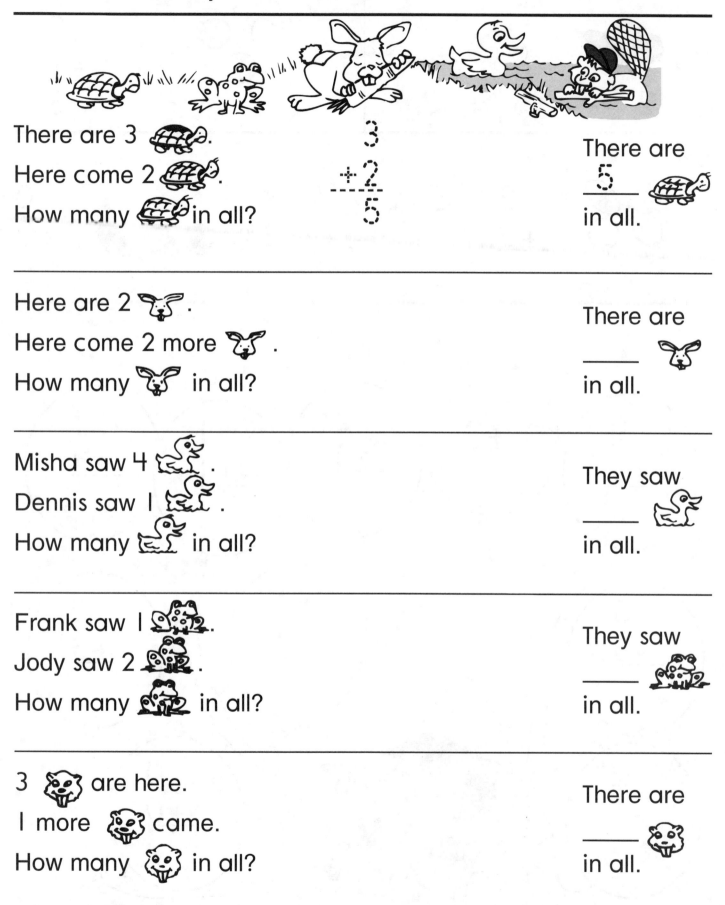

There are 3 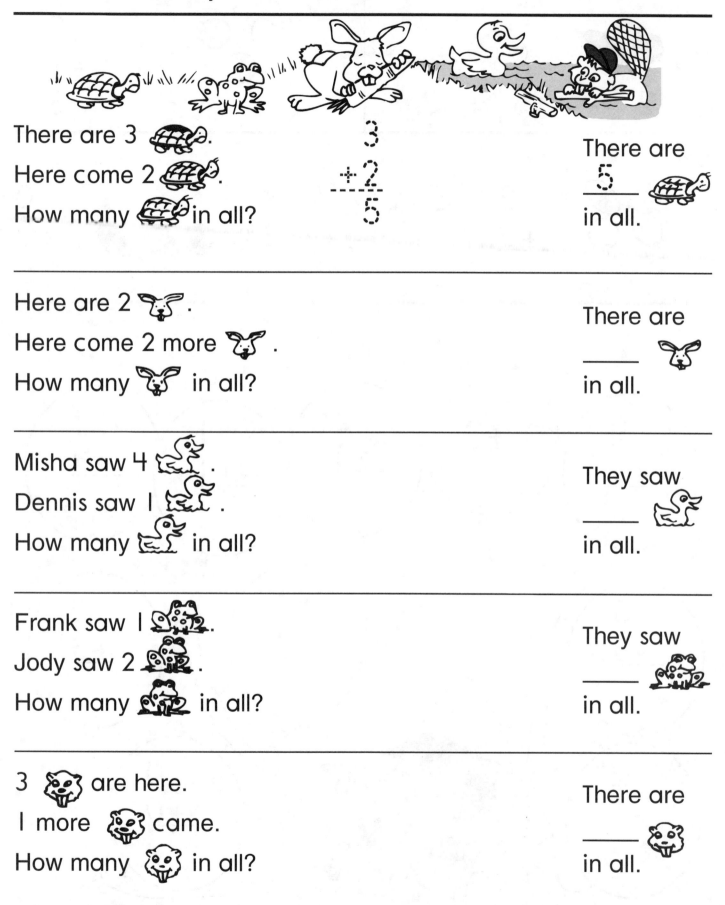.
Here come 2 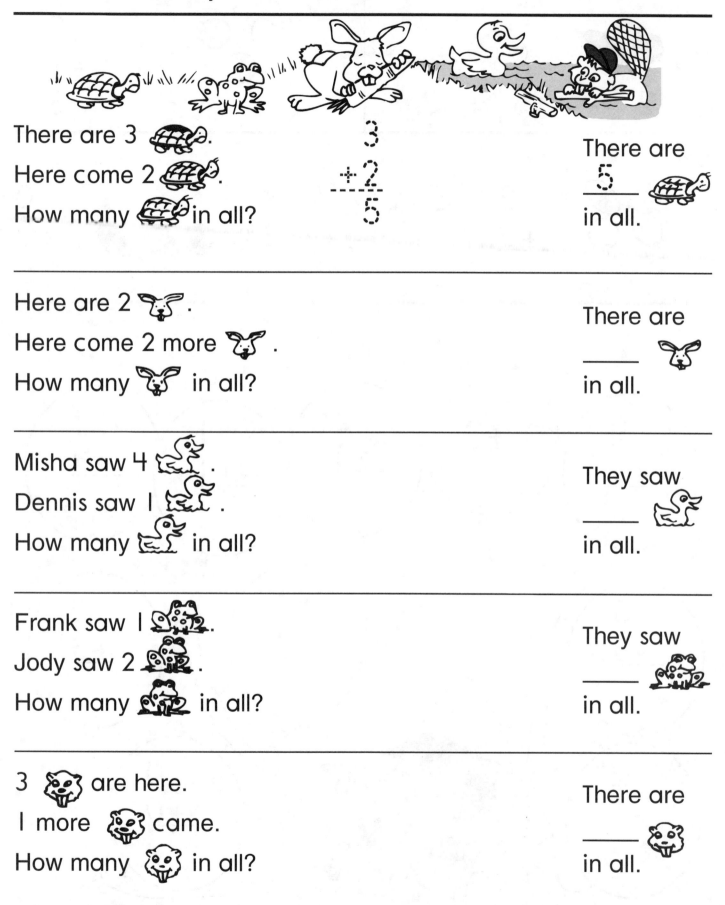.
How many 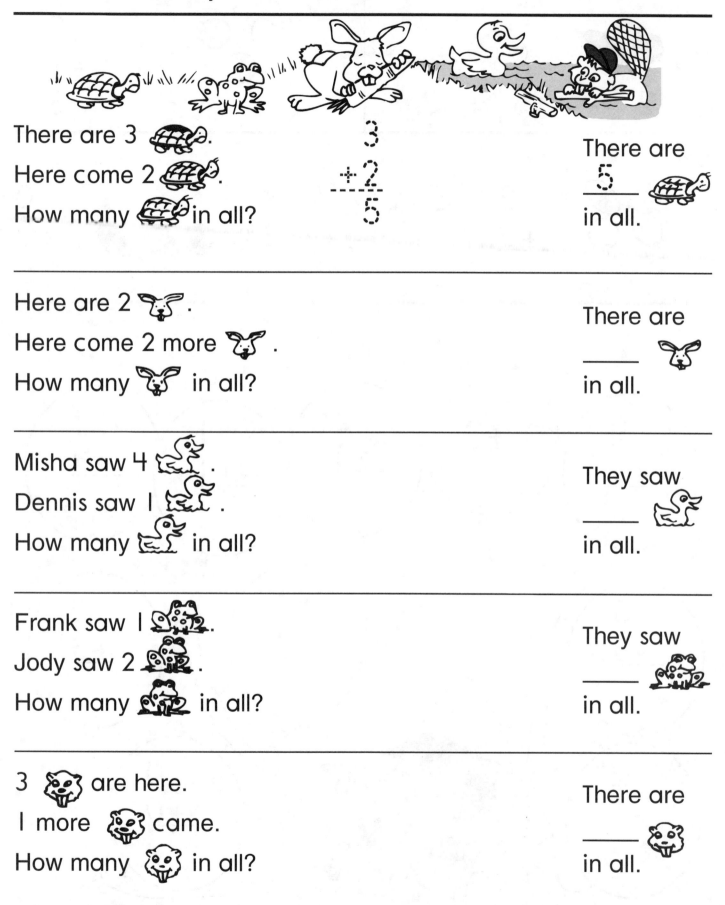 in all?

$$\begin{array}{r} 3 \\ +\,2 \\ \hline 5 \end{array}$$

There are
5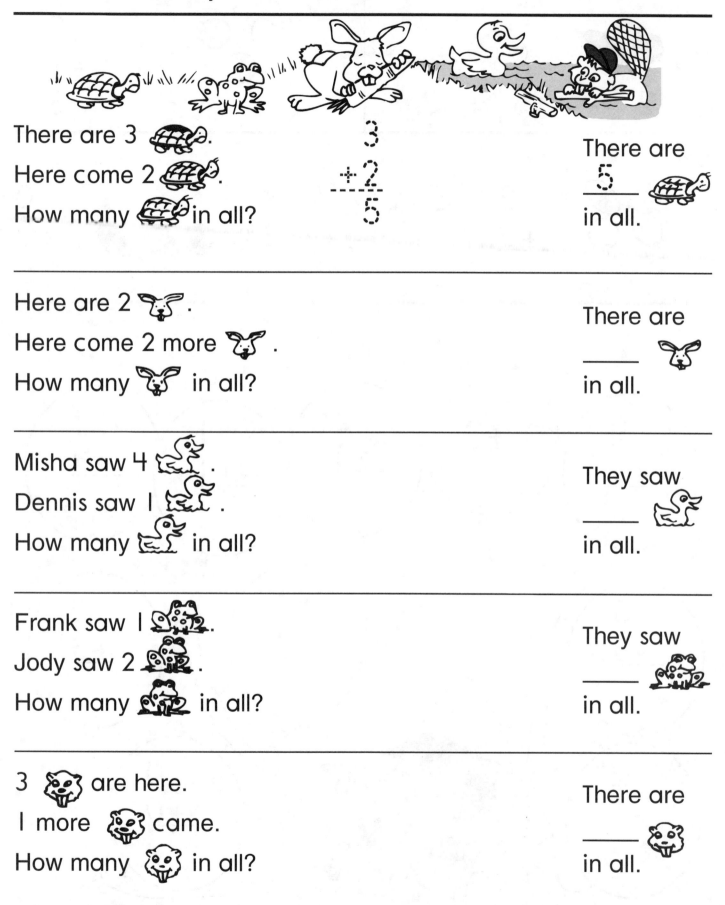
in all.

Here are 2 .
Here come 2 more .
How many in all?

There are
___
in all.

Misha saw 4 .
Dennis saw 1 .
How many in all?

They saw
___
in all.

Frank saw 1 .
Jody saw 2 .
How many in all?

They saw
___
in all.

3 are here.
1 more came.
How many in all?

There are
___
in all.

Problem Solving: Addition

Add.

5 + 1 = _6_

4 + 2 = ___

3
+3
___
6

6
+0
___

2
+4
___

Add.

1 + 5 = ___

2 + 3 = ___

0 + 6 = ___

2
+2
___

5
+1
___

1
+0
___

4
+2
___

3
+3
___

1
+2
___

🐿 has 4 🌰 .
She finds 1 more 🌰 .
How many 🌰 in all?

4
+1
___

2 🐿 are in a tree.
4 more 🐿 come.
How many 🐿 now?

Add.

6 + 1 = _7_   5 + 2 = ___

4   7   2
+3   +0   +5
_7_

Add.

1 + 6 = ___   3 + 2 = ___   0 + 7 = ___

3   4   6   3   2   5
+4   +1   +1   +3   +4   +2

Elena has 3 .

She gets 4 more .

How many now?

Charlie gets 1 .

Ling gets 5 .

How many in all?

Addition: Facts for 7

Add.

7 + 1 = __8__   6 + 2 = ____

5   4   8
+3   +4   +0
8

Add.

2 + 6 = ____   1 + 7 = ____   3 + 3 = ____

4   1   0   4   3   7
+4   +6   +8   +2   +5   +1

has 5 blue ✿ .

He has 3 red ✿ .

How many ✿ in all?

_____

2 are running.

3 more come.

How many now?

Add.

$8 + 1 = \underline{9}$ $7 + 2 = \underline{}$

$\begin{array}{r} 6 \\ +3 \\ \hline 9 \end{array}$ $\begin{array}{r} 5 \\ +4 \\ \hline \end{array}$ $\begin{array}{r} 0 \\ +9 \\ \hline \end{array}$

Add.

$1 + 8 = \underline{}$ $3 + 6 = \underline{}$ $2 + 5 = \underline{}$

$\begin{array}{r} 4 \\ +5 \\ \hline \end{array}$ $\begin{array}{r} 8 \\ +1 \\ \hline \end{array}$ $\begin{array}{r} 2 \\ +7 \\ \hline \end{array}$ $\begin{array}{r} 3 \\ +4 \\ \hline \end{array}$ $\begin{array}{r} 9 \\ +0 \\ \hline \end{array}$ $\begin{array}{r} 6 \\ +3 \\ \hline \end{array}$

Iris colored 4 ▨.

Jeff colored 5 ▨.

How many ▨ in all?

Brad has 4 ✎.

Amy gives him 4 more ✎.

How many ✎ now?

38

Add.

9 + 1 = $\underline{10}$

8 + 2 = _____

7
+3
$\underline{10}$

6
+4

5
+5

Add.

1 + 9 = ___   3 + 5 = ___   0 + 10 = ___

4
+6

5
+2

10
+ 0

5
+4

3
+7

2
+8

6 🔵 are in a bag.

Yoshi puts in 4 more 🔵.

How many 🔵 now?

Pedro has 7 🔵.

Katy has 3 🔵.

How many 🔵 in all?

Add. Find each score.

$$\begin{array}{r} 4 \\ +2 \\ \hline \end{array}$$

Add.

$$\begin{array}{r} 2 \\ +1 \\ \hline \end{array}$$
$$\begin{array}{r} 4 \\ +3 \\ \hline \end{array}$$
$$\begin{array}{r} 7 \\ +2 \\ \hline \end{array}$$
$$\begin{array}{r} 10 \\ +\ 0 \\ \hline \end{array}$$
$$\begin{array}{r} 1 \\ +8 \\ \hline \end{array}$$
$$\begin{array}{r} 5 \\ +2 \\ \hline \end{array}$$

$$\begin{array}{r} 2 \\ +8 \\ \hline \end{array}$$
$$\begin{array}{r} 3 \\ +7 \\ \hline \end{array}$$
$$\begin{array}{r} 2 \\ +2 \\ \hline \end{array}$$
$$\begin{array}{r} 6 \\ +1 \\ \hline \end{array}$$
$$\begin{array}{r} 0 \\ +1 \\ \hline \end{array}$$
$$\begin{array}{r} 3 \\ +3 \\ \hline \end{array}$$

$$\begin{array}{r} 2 \\ +7 \\ \hline \end{array}$$
$$\begin{array}{r} 0 \\ +0 \\ \hline \end{array}$$
$$\begin{array}{r} 9 \\ +1 \\ \hline \end{array}$$
$$\begin{array}{r} 3 \\ +1 \\ \hline \end{array}$$
$$\begin{array}{r} 6 \\ +3 \\ \hline \end{array}$$
$$\begin{array}{r} 8 \\ +2 \\ \hline \end{array}$$

Addition Practice: Facts to 10

Write the missing numbers.

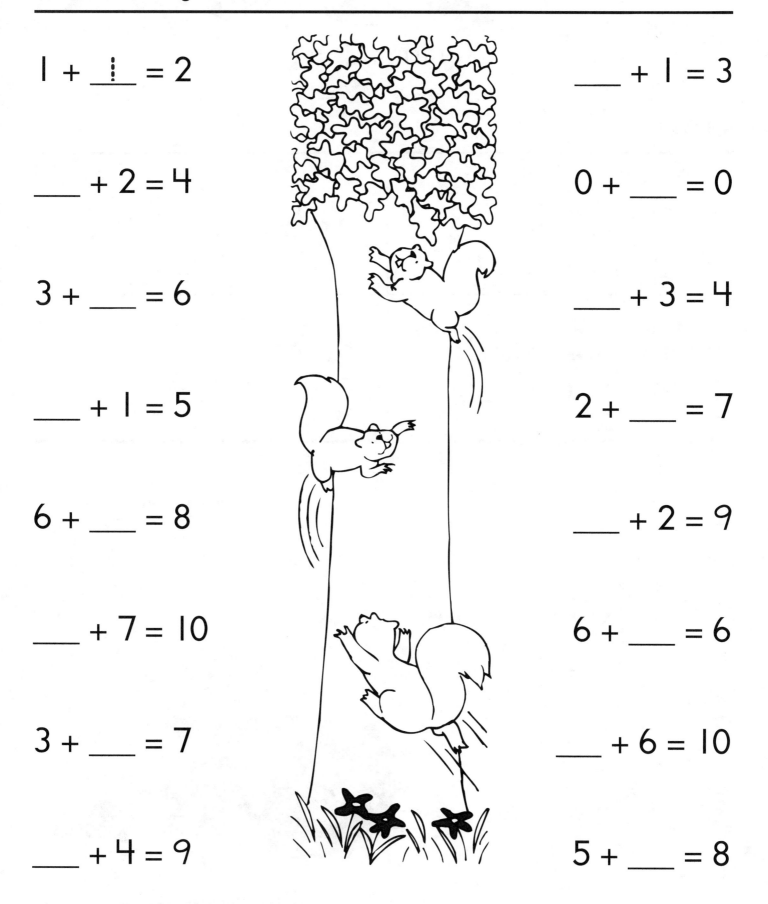

$1 + \underline{1} = 2$

$\underline{} + 2 = 4$

$3 + \underline{} = 6$

$\underline{} + 1 = 5$

$6 + \underline{} = 8$

$\underline{} + 7 = 10$

$3 + \underline{} = 7$

$\underline{} + 4 = 9$

$\underline{} + 1 = 3$

$0 + \underline{} = 0$

$\underline{} + 3 = 4$

$2 + \underline{} = 7$

$\underline{} + 2 = 9$

$6 + \underline{} = 6$

$\underline{} + 6 = 10$

$5 + \underline{} = 8$

3 minus 2 = 1
3 – 2 = 1

Subtract.

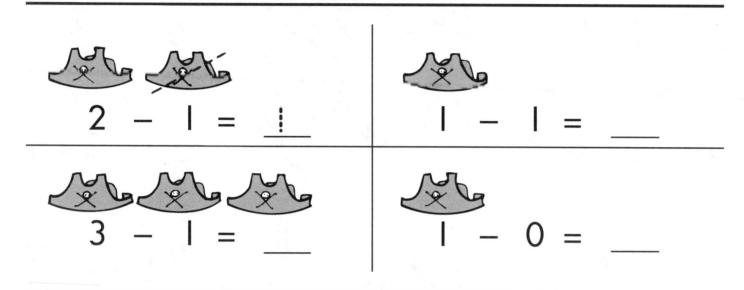

2 – 1 = $\underline{1}$ | 1 – 1 = ___

3 – 1 = ___ | 1 – 0 = ___

Subtract.

2 – 2 = ___   3 – 3 = ___

3 – 0 = ___   0 – 0 = ___

3 – 1 = ___

2 – 0 = ___

3 – 2 = ___

1 – 1 = ___

Introduction to Subtraction: Facts to 3

Subtract.

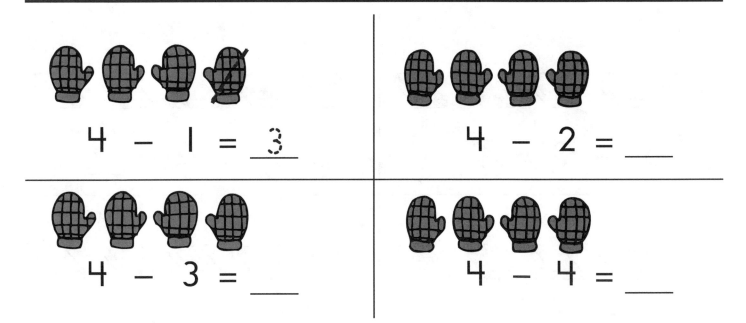

$4 - 1 = \underline{3}$

$4 - 2 = \underline{}$

$4 - 3 = \underline{}$

$4 - 4 = \underline{}$

Subtract.

$4 - 0 = \underline{}$ $3 - 2 = \underline{}$ $4 - 1 = \underline{}$

$2 - 2 = \underline{}$ $4 - 2 = \underline{}$ $3 - 1 = \underline{}$

                       $4 - 4 = \underline{}$ $2 - 1 = \underline{}$

                       $3 - 0 = \underline{}$ $4 - 3 = \underline{}$

Subtract.

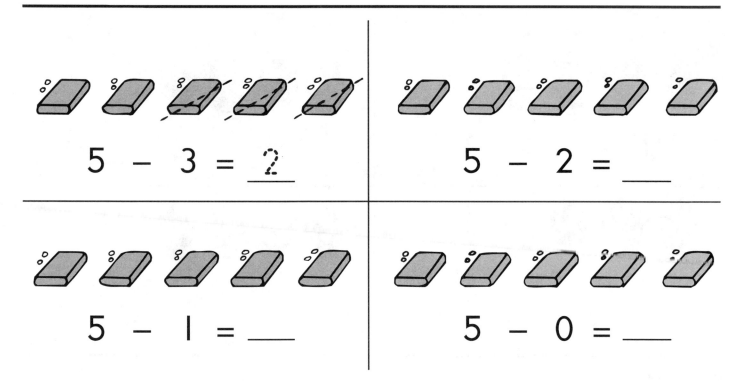

5 − 3 = 2

5 − 2 = ___

5 − 1 = ___

5 − 0 = ___

Subtract.

5 − 4 = ___

4 − 1 = ___

5 − 5 = ___

3 − 2 = ___

5 − 2 = ___

5 − 3 = ___

3 − 1 = ___

5 − 1 = ___

4 − 2 = ___

0 − 0 = ___

Subtraction: Facts for 5

Write subtraction sentences to find how many are left.

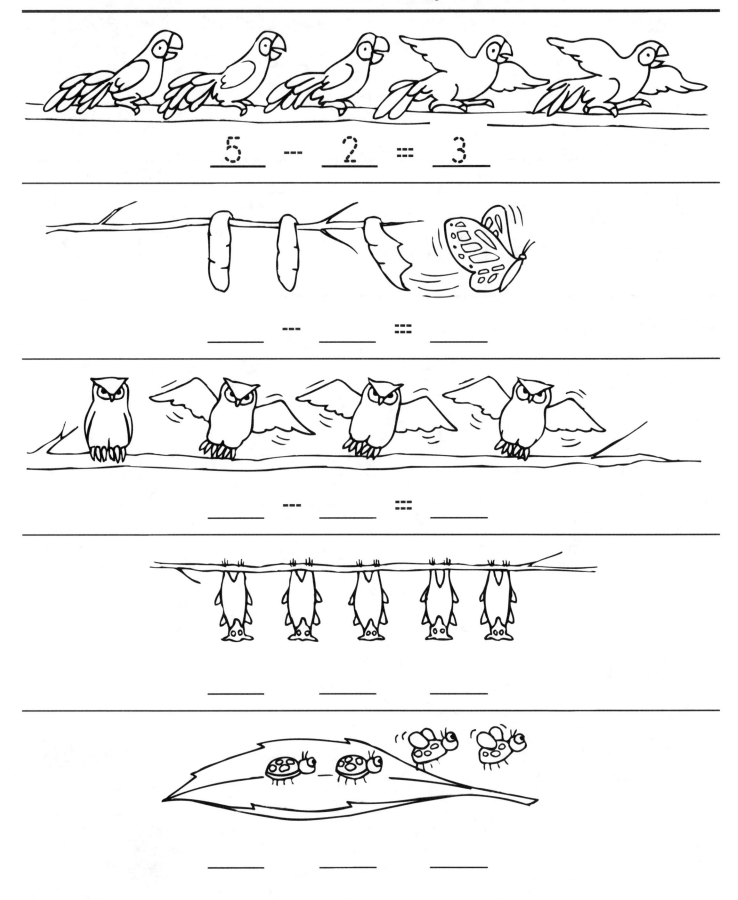

$$5 - 2 = 3$$

___ -- ___ == ___

___ -- ___ == ___

___ -- ___

___ -- ___

$$3 - 1 = \underline{2}$$

$$\begin{array}{r} 3 \\ -1 \\ \hline 2 \end{array}$$

Subtract.

$$\begin{array}{r} 5 \\ -2 \\ \hline 3 \end{array}$$

$$\begin{array}{r} 4 \\ -3 \\ \hline \end{array}$$

$$\begin{array}{r} 3 \\ -0 \\ \hline \end{array}$$

Subtract.

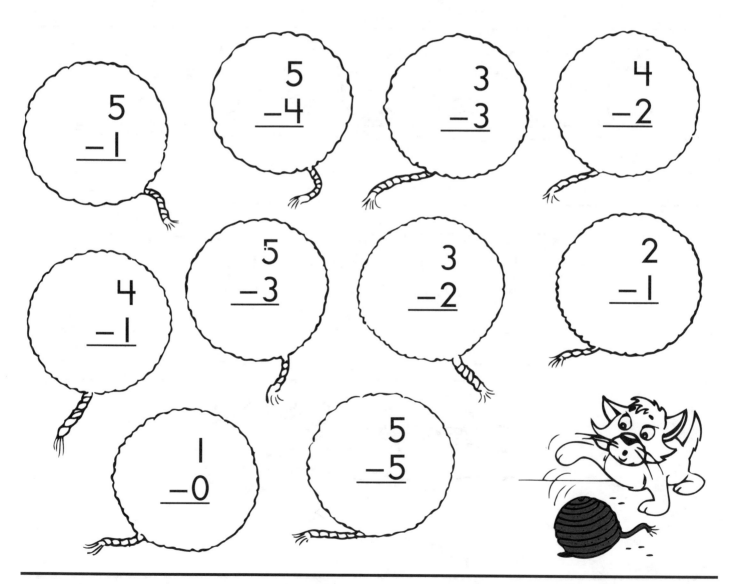

$$\begin{array}{r} 5 \\ -1 \\ \hline \end{array}$$

$$\begin{array}{r} 5 \\ -4 \\ \hline \end{array}$$

$$\begin{array}{r} 3 \\ -3 \\ \hline \end{array}$$

$$\begin{array}{r} 4 \\ -2 \\ \hline \end{array}$$

$$\begin{array}{r} 4 \\ -1 \\ \hline \end{array}$$

$$\begin{array}{r} 5 \\ -3 \\ \hline \end{array}$$

$$\begin{array}{r} 3 \\ -2 \\ \hline \end{array}$$

$$\begin{array}{r} 2 \\ -1 \\ \hline \end{array}$$

$$\begin{array}{r} 1 \\ -0 \\ \hline \end{array}$$

$$\begin{array}{r} 5 \\ -5 \\ \hline \end{array}$$

Subtraction: Vertical Form

Subtract to find how many are left.

Here are 4 🌭.
George eats 2 🌭.
How many 🌭 are left?

$$\begin{array}{r} 4 \\ -2 \\ \hline 2 \end{array}$$

There are 2 🌭 left.

Connie has 5 🍦.
She gives 4 🍦 away.
How many 🍦 are left?

There is ___ 🍦 left.

Henry has 4 🥨.
He eats 0 🥨.
How many 🥨 are left?

There are ___ 🥨 left.

Lily has 2 🍎.
She eats 2 🍎.
How many 🍎 are left?

There are ___ 🍎 left.

Ray buys 4 🥫.
He gives 1 🥫 to Sarah.
How many 🥫 are left?

There are ___ 🥫 left.

Subtract.

6 − 2 = _4_   6 − 5 = ___

$\begin{array}{r} 6 \\ -4 \\ \hline 2 \end{array}$

$\begin{array}{r} 6 \\ -3 \\ \hline \end{array}$

$\begin{array}{r} 6 \\ -1 \\ \hline \end{array}$

Subtract.

6 − 0 = ___   5 − 3 = ___   6 − 6 = ___

$\begin{array}{r} 6 \\ -3 \\ \hline \end{array}$
$\begin{array}{r} 4 \\ -0 \\ \hline \end{array}$
$\begin{array}{r} 6 \\ -4 \\ \hline \end{array}$
$\begin{array}{r} 5 \\ -1 \\ \hline \end{array}$
$\begin{array}{r} 6 \\ -5 \\ \hline \end{array}$
$\begin{array}{r} 4 \\ -3 \\ \hline \end{array}$

has 6 .

breaks 2 .

How many are left?

$\begin{array}{r} 6 \\ -2 \\ \hline \end{array}$

There are 4 .

breaks 2 .

How many now?

Subtract.

7 – 3 = __4__

7 – 6 = ____

$\begin{array}{r} 7 \\ -2 \\ \hline 5 \end{array}$

$\begin{array}{r} 7 \\ -0 \\ \hline \end{array}$

$\begin{array}{r} 7 \\ -7 \\ \hline \end{array}$

Subtract.

7 – 4 = ____   7 – 1 = ____   7 – 5 = ____

$\begin{array}{r} 7 \\ -6 \\ \hline \end{array}$ $\begin{array}{r} 5 \\ -3 \\ \hline \end{array}$ $\begin{array}{r} 7 \\ -2 \\ \hline \end{array}$ $\begin{array}{r} 6 \\ -1 \\ \hline \end{array}$ $\begin{array}{r} 7 \\ -3 \\ \hline \end{array}$ $\begin{array}{r} 6 \\ -4 \\ \hline \end{array}$

7 🐦 are in a cage.

4 🐦 get out.

How many 🐦 are left?

_____

There are 6 🪱.

The 🐦 eat 5 🪱.

How many 🪱 now?

Subtract.

8 – 5 = _3_   8 – 1 = ___

8
−7
∴

8
−6

8
−3

Subtract.

8 – 0 = ___   8 – 2 = ___   8 – 8 = ___

8
−4

7
−3

6
−5

8
−1

8
−3

5
−2

🐊 has 6 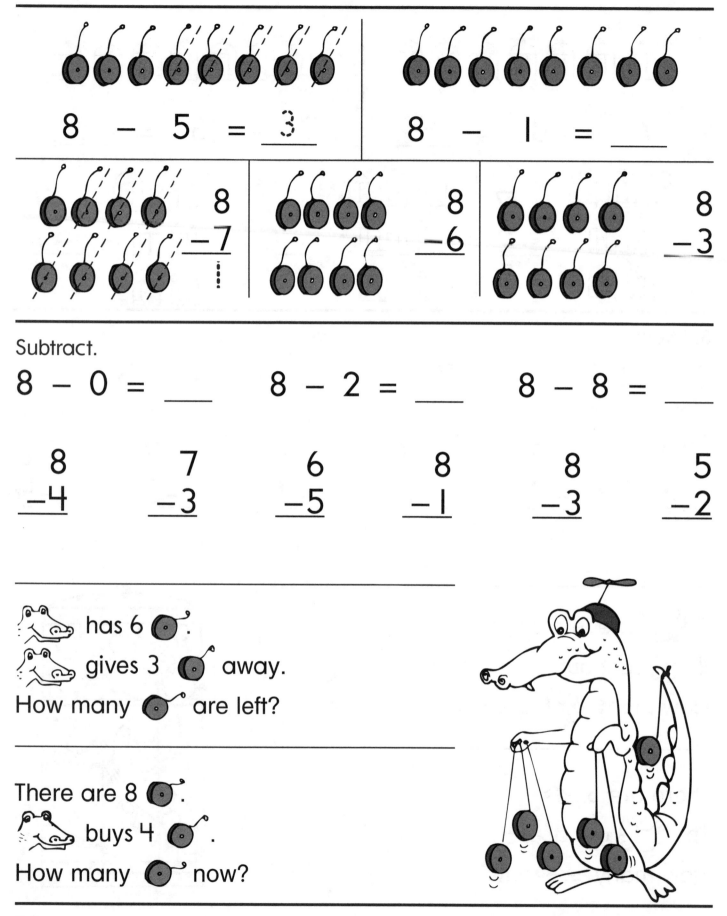.

🐊 gives 3 away.

How many are left?

_____

There are 8 .

🐊 buys 4 .

How many now?

Subtract.

$9 - 4 = 5$ | $9 - 2 = \underline{}$

$\begin{array}{r} 9 \\ -6 \\ \hline 3 \end{array}$ | $\begin{array}{r} 9 \\ -9 \\ \hline \end{array}$ | $\begin{array}{r} 9 \\ -7 \\ \hline \end{array}$

Subtract.

$9 - 5 = \underline{}$ $9 - 3 = \underline{}$ $9 - 2 = \underline{}$

$\begin{array}{r} 9 \\ -8 \\ \hline \end{array}$ $\begin{array}{r} 9 \\ -0 \\ \hline \end{array}$ $\begin{array}{r} 7 \\ -4 \\ \hline \end{array}$ $\begin{array}{r} 9 \\ -1 \\ \hline \end{array}$ $\begin{array}{r} 8 \\ -4 \\ \hline \end{array}$ $\begin{array}{r} 9 \\ -6 \\ \hline \end{array}$

A 🦫 has 8 🌿.

A dog takes 7 🌿.

How many 🌿 now?

_____

There are 9 🦫.

4 🦫 go away.

How many 🦫 are left?

Subtract.

10   –   1   =   9   10   –   4   =   ___

$$\begin{array}{r} 10 \\ -\ 3 \\ \hline 7 \end{array}$$

$$\begin{array}{r} 10 \\ -\ 2 \\ \hline \end{array}$$

$$\begin{array}{r} 10 \\ -\ 5 \\ \hline \end{array}$$

Subtract.

10 – 6 = ___   10 – 10 = ___   10 – 8 = ___

$$\begin{array}{r} 10 \\ -\ 3 \\ \hline \end{array} \qquad \begin{array}{r} 10 \\ -\ 9 \\ \hline \end{array} \qquad \begin{array}{r} 7 \\ -5 \\ \hline \end{array} \qquad \begin{array}{r} 10 \\ -\ 7 \\ \hline \end{array} \qquad \begin{array}{r} 10 \\ -\ 0 \\ \hline \end{array} \qquad \begin{array}{r} 9 \\ -1 \\ \hline \end{array}$$

Melinda has 10 .

She drops 5 .

How many are left?

There are 9 .

Children eat 6 .

How many now?

Subtract. Find the number of petals left on each flower.

$\begin{array}{r} 6 \\ -2 \\ \hline \end{array}$	$\begin{array}{r} 9 \\ -4 \\ \hline \end{array}$	$\begin{array}{r} 7 \\ -\square \\ \hline \end{array}$

Subtract.

$\begin{array}{r} 7 \\ -2 \\ \hline \end{array}$	$\begin{array}{r} 6 \\ -3 \\ \hline \end{array}$	$\begin{array}{r} 9 \\ -3 \\ \hline \end{array}$	$\begin{array}{r} 10 \\ -\ 5 \\ \hline \end{array}$	$\begin{array}{r} 4 \\ -1 \\ \hline \end{array}$	$\begin{array}{r} 6 \\ -5 \\ \hline \end{array}$
$\begin{array}{r} 3 \\ -3 \\ \hline \end{array}$	$\begin{array}{r} 10 \\ -\ 0 \\ \hline \end{array}$	$\begin{array}{r} 9 \\ -7 \\ \hline \end{array}$	$\begin{array}{r} 8 \\ -3 \\ \hline \end{array}$	$\begin{array}{r} 2 \\ -1 \\ \hline \end{array}$	$\begin{array}{r} 10 \\ -\ 2 \\ \hline \end{array}$
$\begin{array}{r} 8 \\ -5 \\ \hline \end{array}$	$\begin{array}{r} 10 \\ -\ 4 \\ \hline \end{array}$	$\begin{array}{r} 7 \\ -4 \\ \hline \end{array}$	$\begin{array}{r} 10 \\ -\ 6 \\ \hline \end{array}$	$\begin{array}{r} 10 \\ -\ 8 \\ \hline \end{array}$	$\begin{array}{r} 9 \\ -2 \\ \hline \end{array}$

Write the missing numbers.

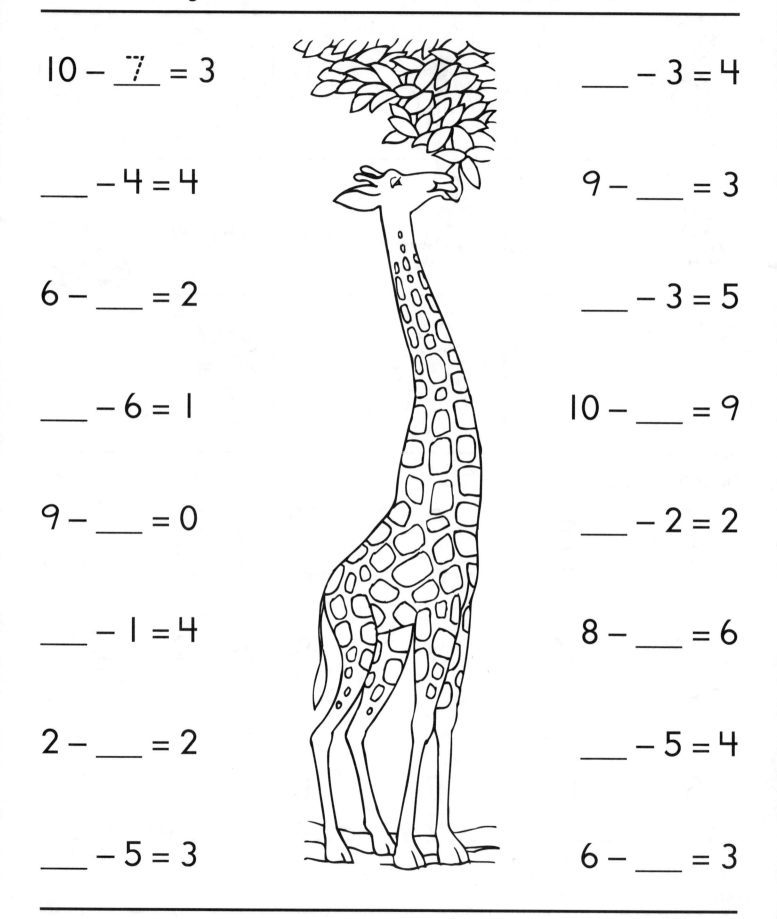

$10 - \underline{7} = 3$

$\underline{} - 4 = 4$

$6 - \underline{} = 2$

$\underline{} - 6 = 1$

$9 - \underline{} = 0$

$\underline{} - 1 = 4$

$2 - \underline{} = 2$

$\underline{} - 5 = 3$

$\underline{} - 3 = 4$

$9 - \underline{} = 3$

$\underline{} - 3 = 5$

$10 - \underline{} = 9$

$\underline{} - 2 = 2$

$8 - \underline{} = 6$

$\underline{} - 5 = 4$

$6 - \underline{} = 3$

Problem Solving: Missing Numbers

Add or subtract.

4 + 3 = ___	6 2	2 + 7 = ___
3 + 4 = ___	+2 +6	9 − 7 = ___
7 − 3 = ___		7 + 2 = ___
7 − 4 = ___	8 8	9 − 2 = ___
	−6 −2	

3 9	10 − 4 = ___	8 8
+6 −3	6 + 4 = ___	−3 −5
	4 + 6 = ___	
9 6	10 − 6 = ___	5 3
−6 +3		+3 +5

Write + or − in each box.

10 ☐ 2 = 8   7 ☐ 5 = 2

2 ☐ 8 = 10   2 ☐ 5 = 7

10 ☐ 8 = 2   7 ☐ 2 = 5

8 ☐ 2 = 10   5 ☐ 2 = 7

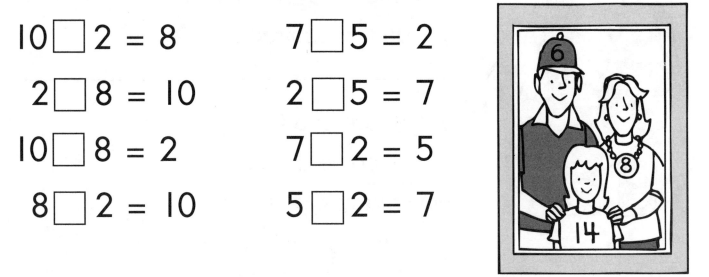

Step 1. Read

Step 2. Think

What do I know?

What must I find out?

What should I do?

Circle **add** or **subtract**.

Step 3. Solve

Write the problem and find the answer.

Step 4. Check

Is 8 a good answer?

2 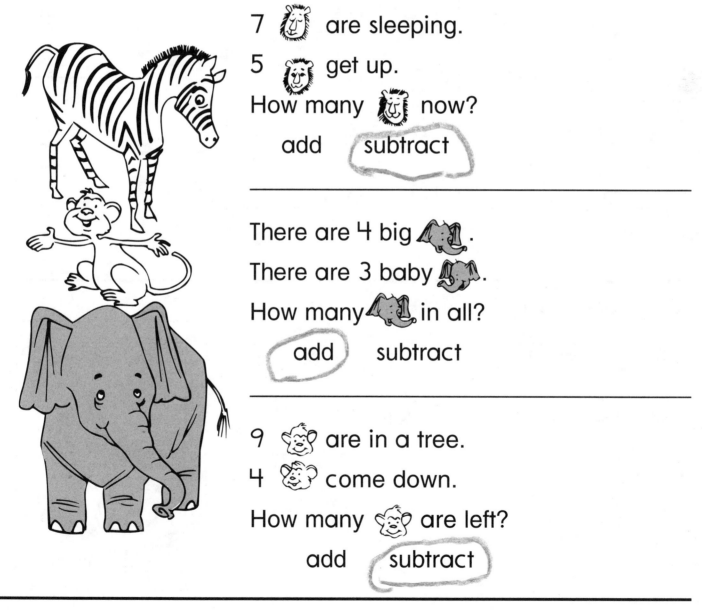 are eating.

6 more come.

How many now?

(add) subtract

$$\begin{array}{r} 2 \\ + 6 \\ \hline 8 \end{array}$$

7 are sleeping.

5 get up.

How many now?

add (subtract)

There are 4 big .

There are 3 baby .

How many in all?

(add) subtract

9 are in a tree.

4 come down.

How many are left?

add (subtract)

Problem Solving: Choosing the Operation

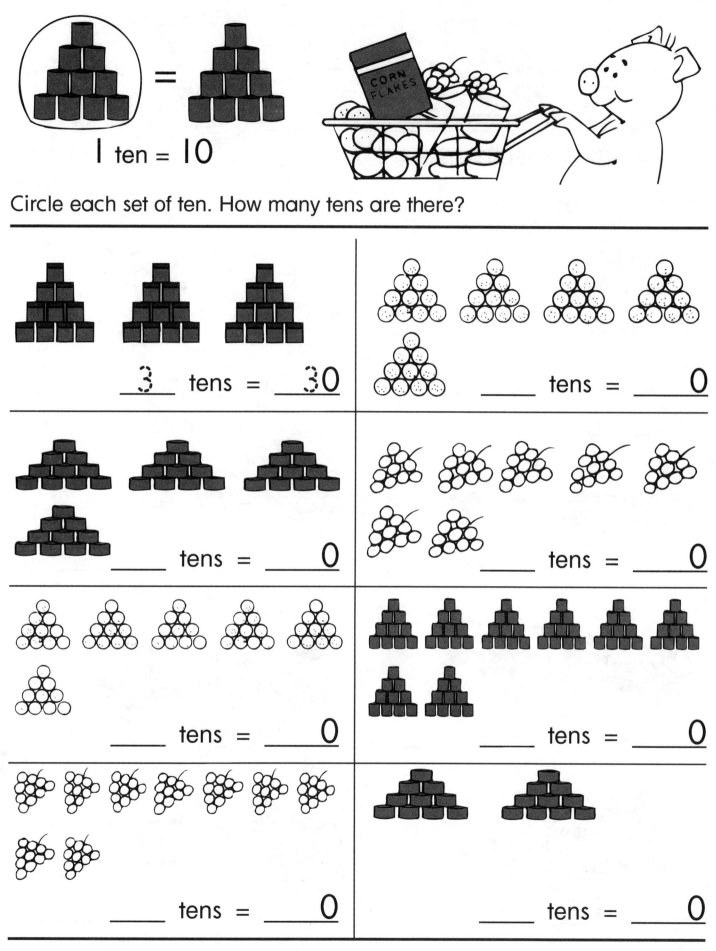

I ten = 10

Circle each set of ten. How many tens are there?

____3____ tens = ____30____

____ tens = ____0____

____ tens = ____0____

____ tens = ____0____

____ tens = ____0____

____ tens = ____0____

____ tens = ____0____

____ tens = ____0____

Tens

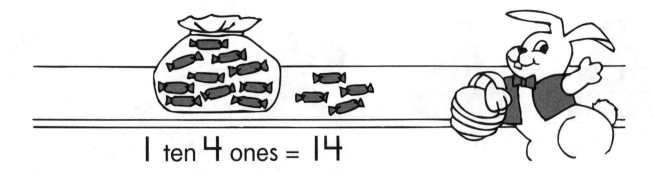

1 ten 4 ones = 14

Write the number of tens and ones.

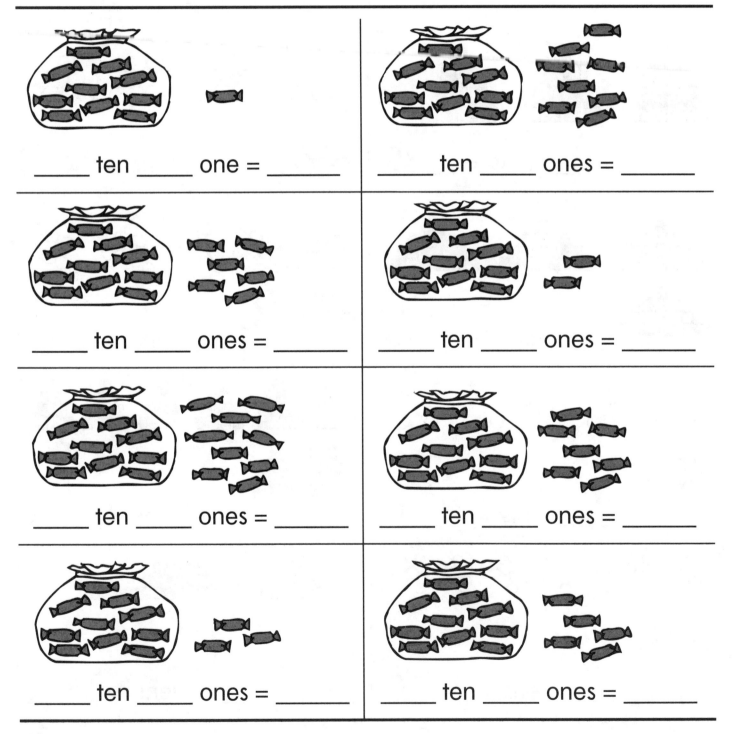

____ ten ____ one = _____

____ ten ____ ones = _____

____ ten ____ ones = _____

____ ten ____ ones = _____

____ ten ____ ones = _____

____ ten ____ ones = _____

____ ten ____ ones = _____

____ ten ____ ones = _____

Tens and Ones

Match.

13   nineteen

11   fifteen

14   thirteen

19   twelve

15   sixteen

16   fourteen

18   eleven

12   eighteen

17   seventeen

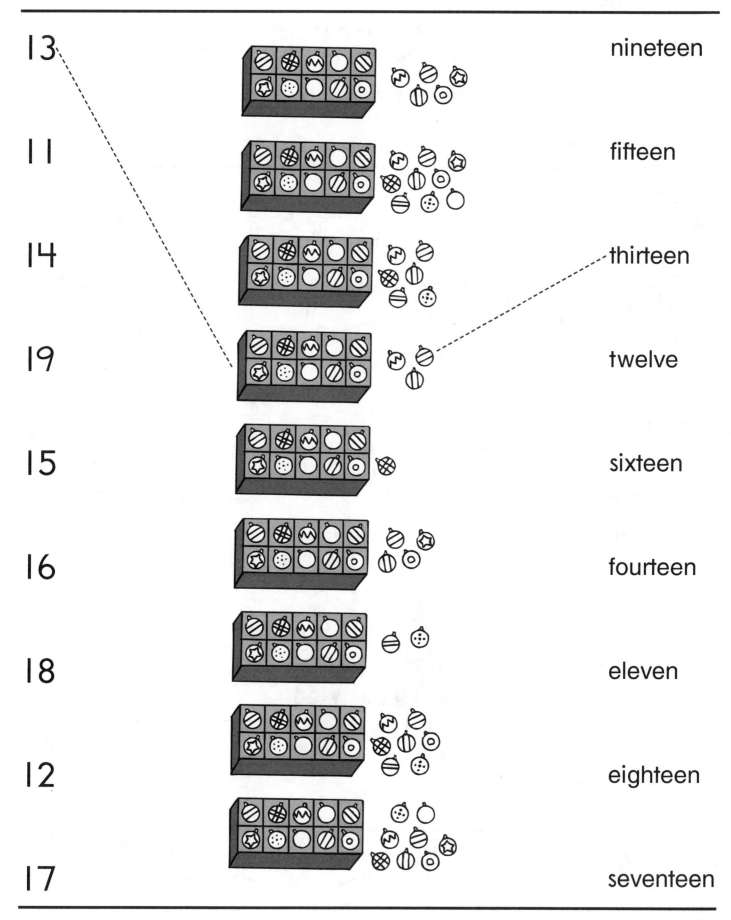

12 comes before 13.

14 comes after 13.

13 comes between 12 and 14.

Write the missing numbers.

Order: Before, After, Between

Write numbers to tell how many.

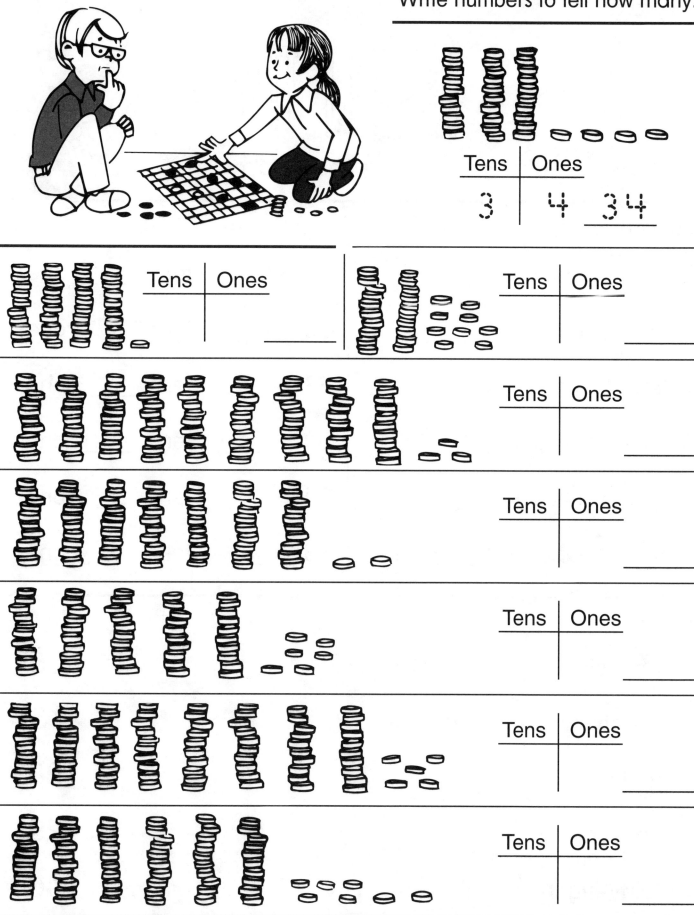

Tens	Ones	
3	4	34

Tens	Ones

Tens	Ones

Tens	Ones

Tens	Ones

Tens	Ones

Tens	Ones

Tens	Ones

Tens and Ones

3 tens 4 ones $= 34$

Complete.

2 tens 1 one = _____   49 = ____ tens ____ ones

4 tens 5 ones = _____   32 = ____ tens ____ ones

1 ten 9 ones = _____   28 = ____ tens ____ ones

3 tens 7 ones = _____   30 = ____ tens ____ ones

2 tens 6 ones = _____   24 = ____ tens ____ ones

4 tens 0 ones = _____   43 = ____ tens ____ ones

Match.

forty-six   35

twenty-nine   16

thirty-five   38

sixteen   29

thirty-eight   46

Write the missing numbers.

0 _ _ _ _ _ _ _ 8 _

_ _ 12 _ _ _ 16 _ _ _

20 _ _ _ _ _ _ 27 _ _

_ 31 _ _ 34 _ _ _ _ _

40 _ _ _ _ _ _ _ _ 49

32 _ _ _ _

_ _ 20 _ _

24 _ _ _ _ 29 _ _ _ _

_ _ 41 _ _ _ _ 46 _ _

$$5 \text{ tens } 2 \text{ ones} = 52$$

Complete.

6 tens 3 ones = _____   79 = ____ tens ____ ones

8 tens 4 ones = _____   65 = ____ tens ____ ones

7 tens 0 ones = _____   8 = ____ tens ____ ones

9 tens 7 ones = _____   57 = ____ tens ____ ones

3 tens 1 one = _____   81 = ____ tens ____ one

5 tens 8 ones = _____   96 = ____ tens ____ ones

Match.

ninty-nine   62

fifty-one   86

seventy-five   51

eighty-six   75

sixty-two   99

Write the missing numbers.

	1								
			13						
		22							
							37		
					45				
									59
						66			
	71								
					84				
90									

What was in the box?
Connect the dots. Start at **50**.

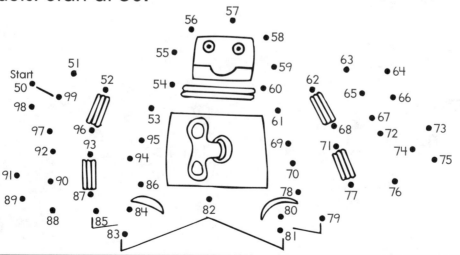

31 is less than **53**   **45** is greater than **22**

Circle the number that is **greater**.

66	(74)	17	11	52	36	29	49
87	62	99	93	44	81	75	97
22	38	56	41				

Circle the number that is **less**.

(19)	25	80	90		
10	0	77	69	33	51
84	96	62	71	59	58

Circle the correct answer.

Annie picked 21 🍎.

Mario picked 29 🍎.

Who picked more 🍎?

Annie   or   Mario

Comparing Numbers

Look at this picture graph.

Person	Number of Fish Caught Today $\rightarrow$ = 1 fish
	Number of Fish
Amy	🐟 🐟 🐟 🐟
Ben	🐟 🐟 🐟 🐟 🐟 🐟 🐟
Carrie	🐟 🐟 🐟 🐟 🐟
Don	🐟 🐟 🐟 🐟 🐟 🐟
Emma	🐟 🐟 🐟
Pham	🐟 🐟

Write how many fish each person caught.

Amy _____   Carrie _____   Emma _____

Ben _____   Don _____   Pham _____

Circle the correct answer.

Who caught more?	Who caught less?
Ben or Don	Carrie or Pham
Amy or Emma	Emma or Ben

| 10 | 20 | 30 | 40 | 50 | 60 | 70 | 80 | 90 |

Write the missing numbers. Count by 10s.

<u>0</u> __ __ __ __ __ <u>70</u> __ __

<u>50</u> __ __ __ __ | <u>20</u> __ __ __

<u>40</u> __ __ __ __ | <u>30</u> __ __ __

Connect the dots. Count by 10s.

| 5 | 10 | 15 | 20 | 25 | 30 | 35 | 40 |

Write the missing numbers. Count by 5s.

10	__	__	__	35	__	__	__
45	__	__	__	__	__	__	95
60	__	__	__	__		25	__	__	__
5	__	__	__	__		75	__	__	__

Connect the dots. Count by 5s.

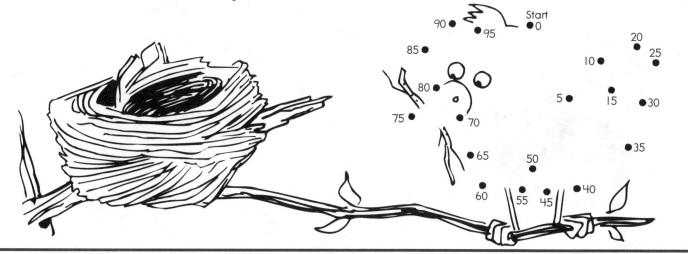

2   4   6   8   10   12

Write the missing numbers. Count by 2s.

2	__	__	__	__	__	14	__	__	__
60	__	__	__	__	__	__	78	__
88	__	__	__	40	__	__	__	__
0	__	__	__	56	__	__	__	__
10	__	__	__	74	__	__	__	__

Connect the dots. Count by 2s.

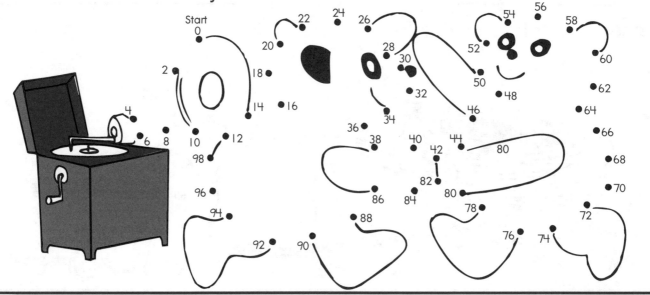

minute hand →

hour hand →

4 o'clock
4:00

Write each time.

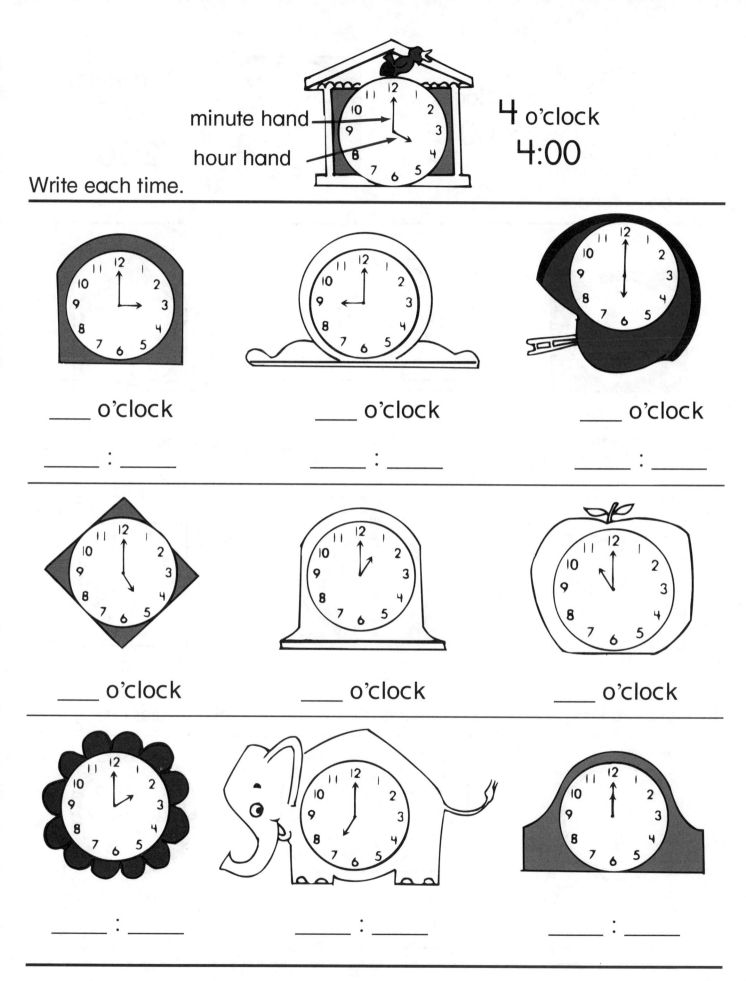

___ o'clock

____ : ____

___ o'clock

____ : ____

___ o'clock

____ : ____

___ o'clock

___ o'clock

___ o'clock

____ : ____

____ : ____

____ : ____

  **2 o'clock**
2:00

 **30 minutes**
after 2
2:30

Write each time.

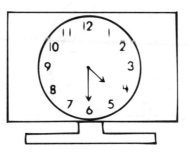

30 minutes after _____

30 minutes after _____

30 minutes after _____

_____ : _____

_____ : _____

_____ : _____

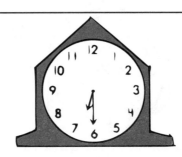

30 minutes after _____

30 minutes after _____

30 minutes after _____

_____ : _____

_____ : _____

_____ : _____

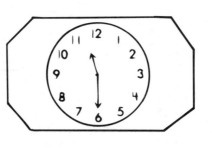

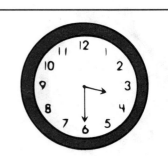

_____ : _____

_____ : _____

_____ : _____

Time: Half Hour

Draw hands on the clocks to show each time.

7:00

7:30

8:30

12:00

3:00

5:30

9:30

Write how many hours later.

___ hours

___ hours

___ hours

___ hours

Problem Solving: Finding Elapsed Time

front   back

Penny
|¢

Write the number of cents.

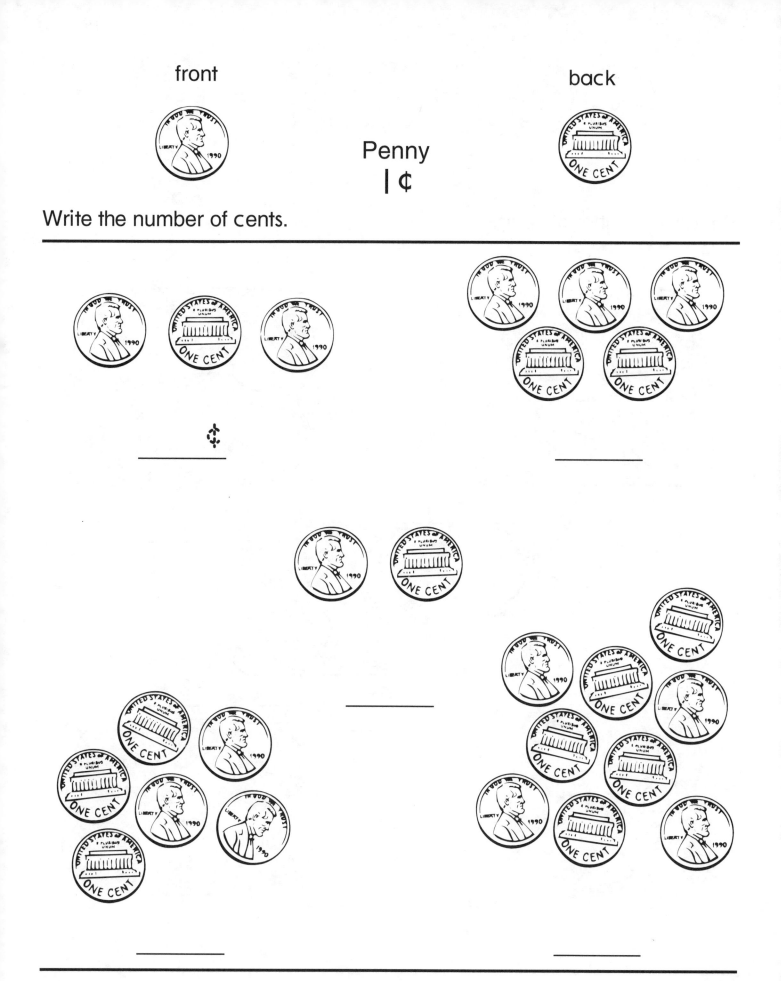

_____ ¢

_____

_____

_____   _____

5¢

Nickel
5¢

Write the number of cents.

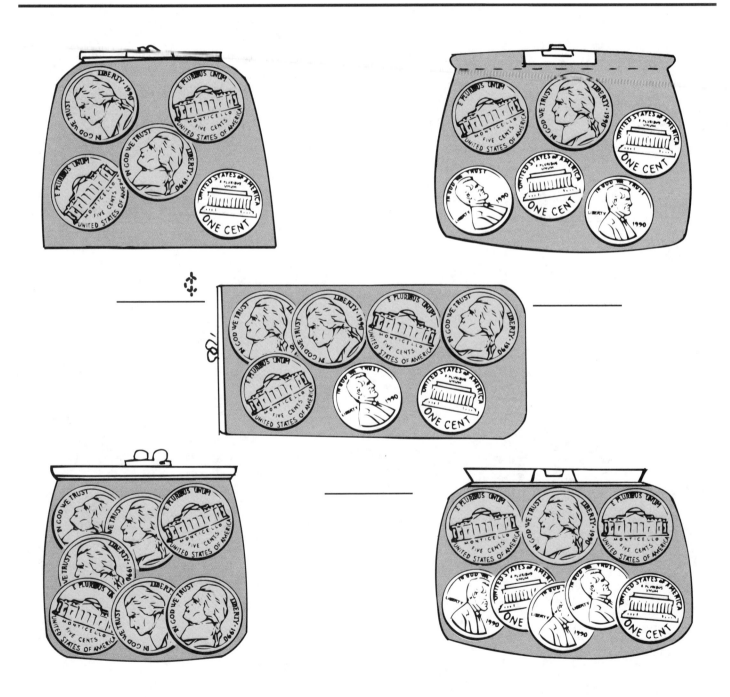

76

10¢   10¢   Dime
                                    10¢

Match.

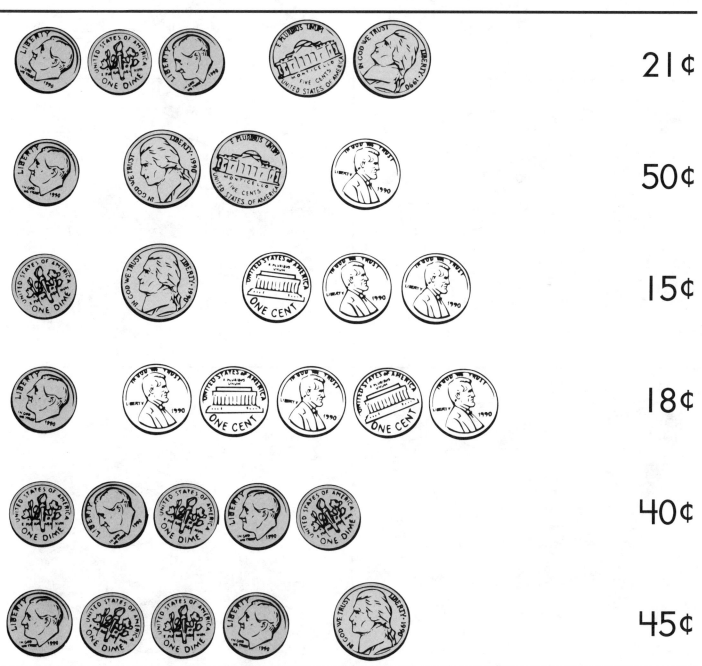

21¢

50¢

15¢

18¢

40¢

45¢

Mark enough coins to make the correct amount.

Problem Solving: Using Money

Mark the one that comes next.

Draw each shape.

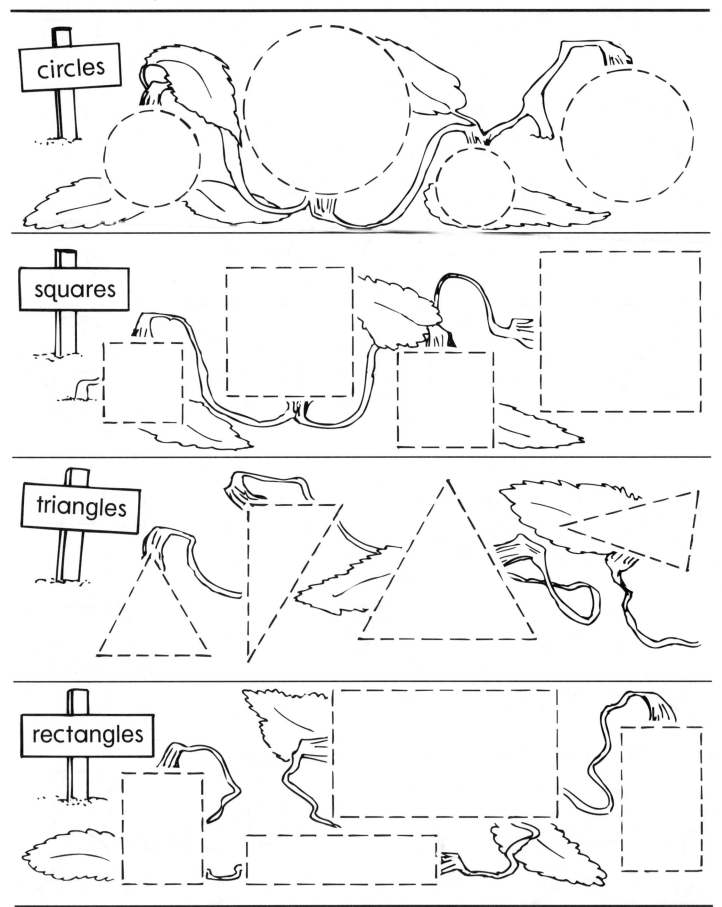

circles

squares

triangles

rectangles

Geometry: Plane Figures

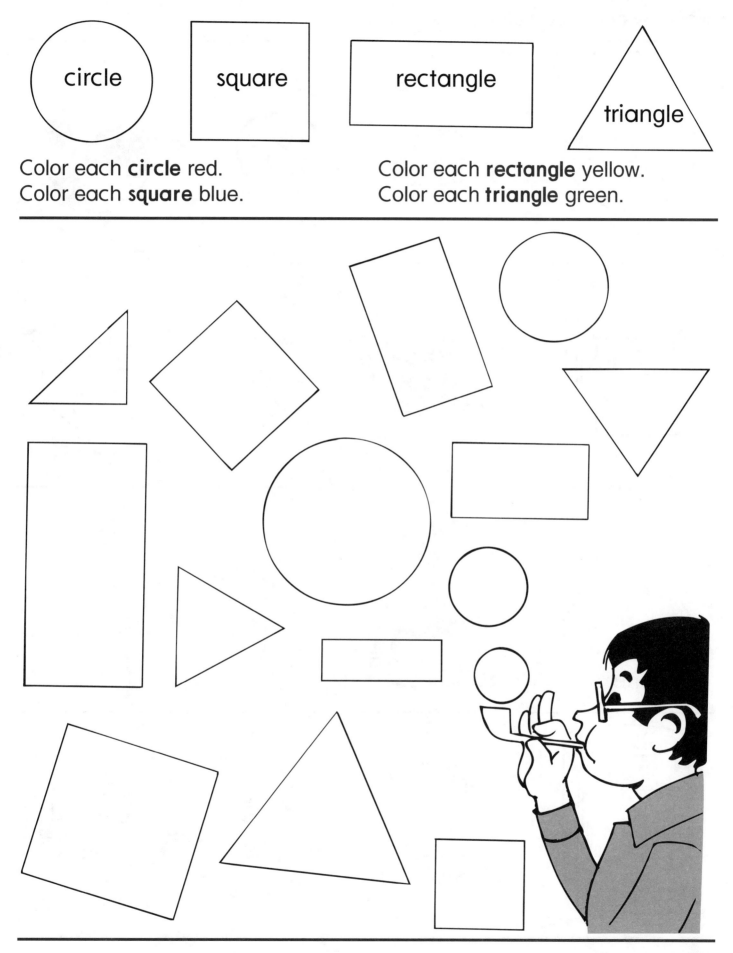

circle

square

rectangle

triangle

Color each **circle** red.
Color each **square** blue.

Color each **rectangle** yellow.
Color each **triangle** green.

Mark the objects with the same shape.

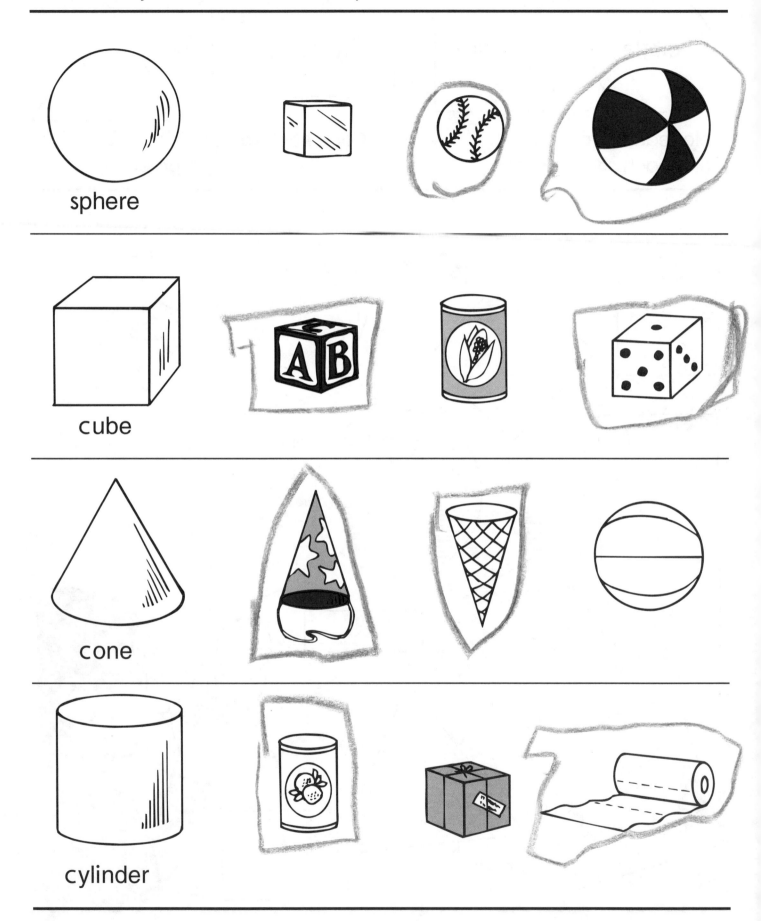

sphere

cube

cone

cylinder

Geometry: Solid Figures

**If this shape is folded,
the two parts match.**

Mark each shape that has matching parts when it is folded.

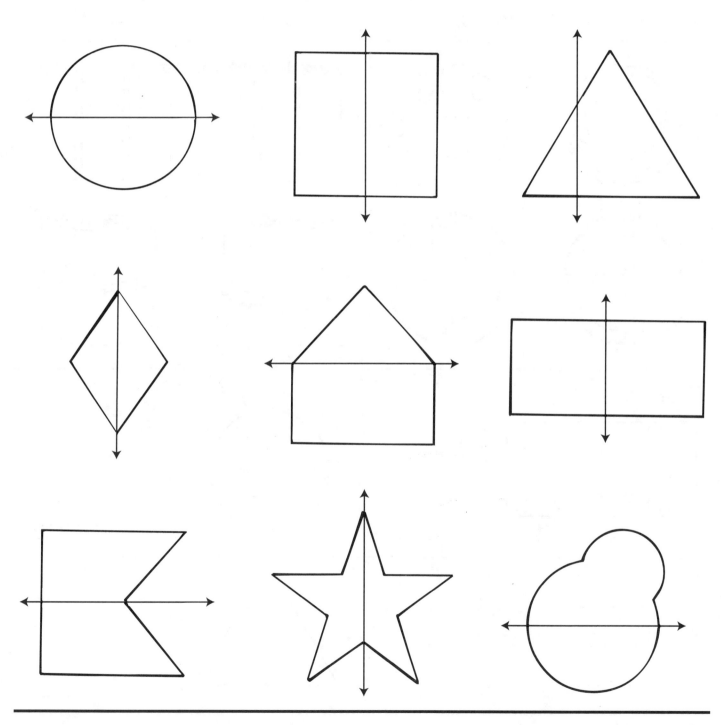

4 equal parts

Mark the one with **equal parts**.

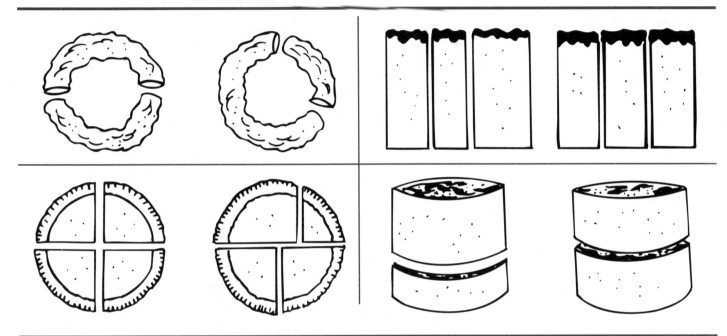

Write the number of equal parts.

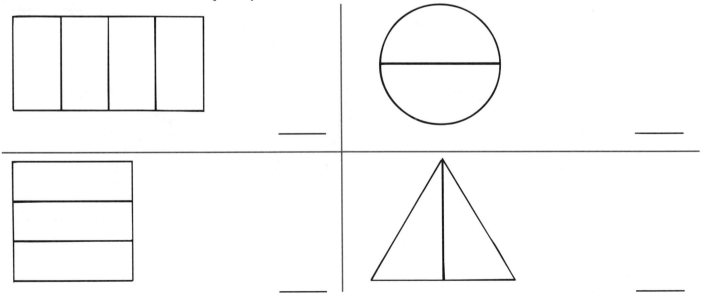

_____   _____

_____   _____

Fractions: Equal Parts

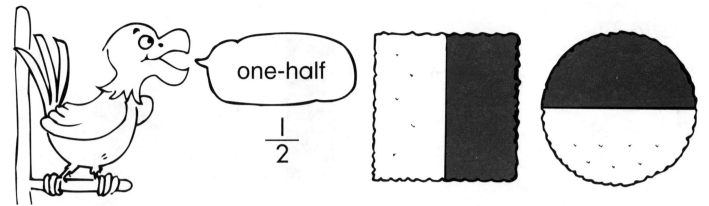

one-half

$\frac{1}{2}$

Mark the figures that show **one-half**.

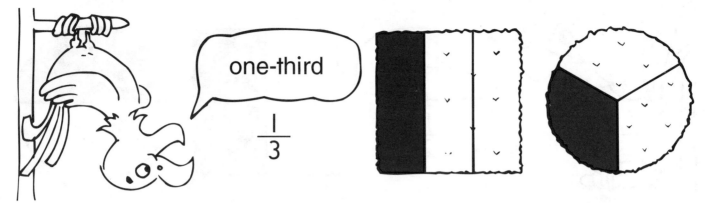

one-third

$\dfrac{1}{3}$

Mark the figures that show one-third.

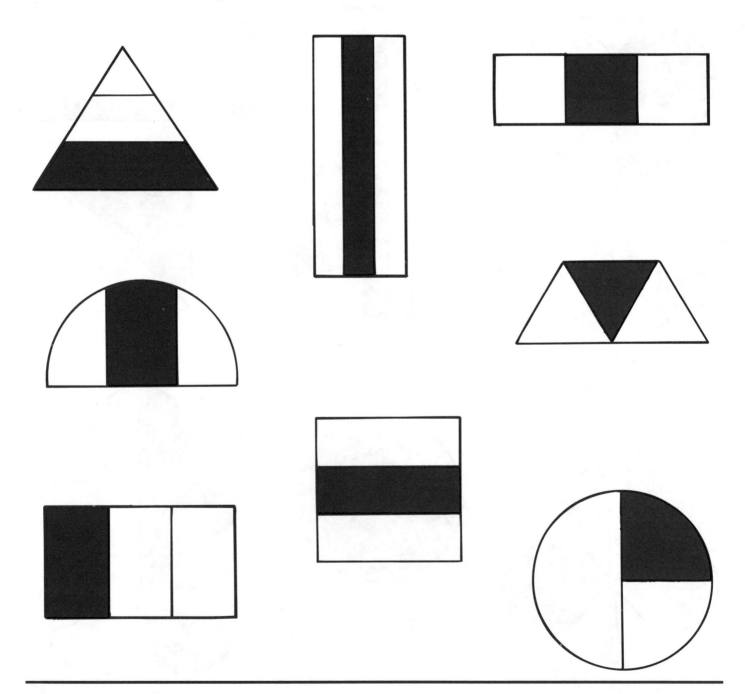

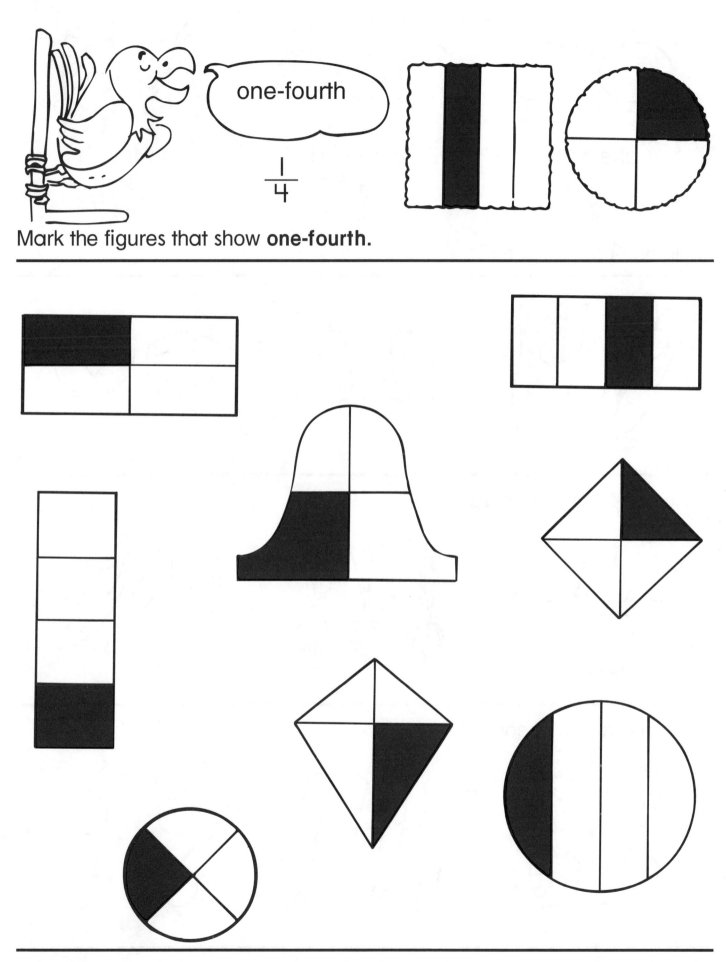

Mark the figures that show **one-fourth**.

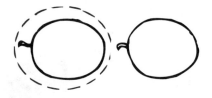
one-half

$\dfrac{1}{2}$

one-third

$\dfrac{1}{3}$

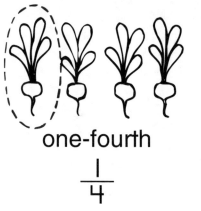
one-fourth

$\dfrac{1}{4}$

Circle **one-half** of each set.

Circle **one-third** of each set.

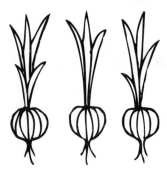

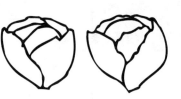

Circle **one-fourth** of each set.

Circle the correct fraction.

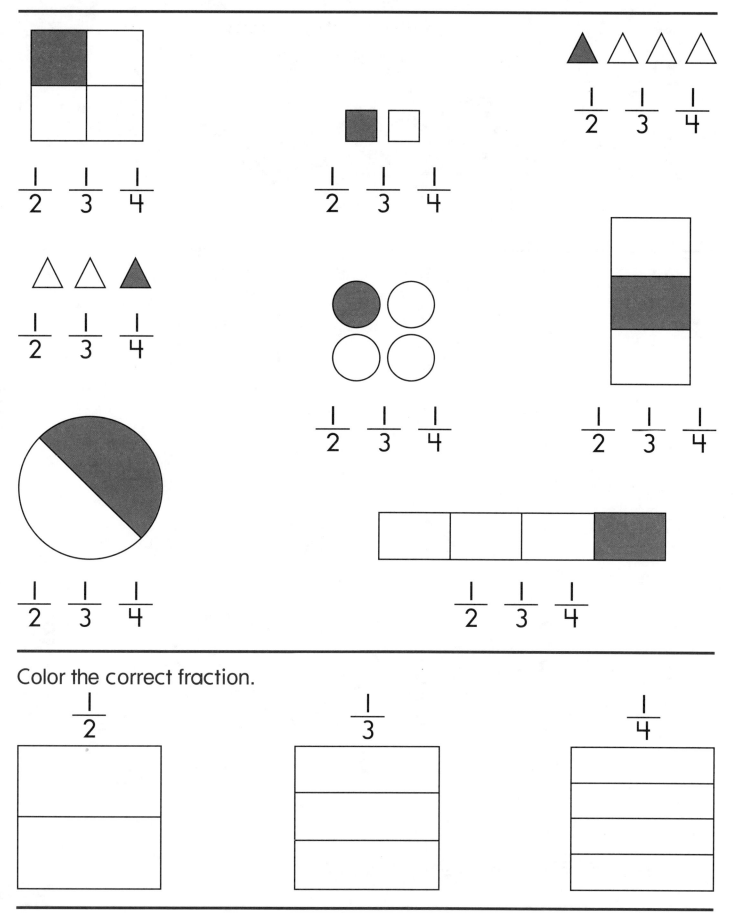

$\dfrac{1}{2}$ $\dfrac{1}{3}$ $\dfrac{1}{4}$

$\dfrac{1}{2}$ $\dfrac{1}{3}$ $\dfrac{1}{4}$

$\dfrac{1}{2}$ $\dfrac{1}{3}$ $\dfrac{1}{4}$

$\dfrac{1}{2}$ $\dfrac{1}{3}$ $\dfrac{1}{4}$

$\dfrac{1}{2}$ $\dfrac{1}{3}$ $\dfrac{1}{4}$

$\dfrac{1}{2}$ $\dfrac{1}{3}$ $\dfrac{1}{4}$

$\dfrac{1}{2}$ $\dfrac{1}{3}$ $\dfrac{1}{4}$

$\dfrac{1}{2}$ $\dfrac{1}{3}$ $\dfrac{1}{4}$

Color the correct fraction.

$\dfrac{1}{2}$ $\dfrac{1}{3}$ $\dfrac{1}{4}$

Fractions Practice

You can add the numbers two ways.

$$\begin{array}{r} 2 \\ 3 \\ +4 \\ \hline 9 \end{array}$$ 5 ∶∷

$$\begin{array}{r} 2 \\ 3 \\ +4 \\ \hline 9 \end{array}$$ 7 ∷∷

Add.

$$\begin{array}{r} 2 \\ 3 \\ +3 \\ \hline \end{array}$$ $$\begin{array}{r} 2 \\ 3 \\ +3 \\ \hline \end{array}$$ $$\begin{array}{r} 5 \\ 2 \\ +3 \\ \hline \end{array}$$ $$\begin{array}{r} 5 \\ 2 \\ +3 \\ \hline \end{array}$$ $$\begin{array}{r} 1 \\ 1 \\ +5 \\ \hline \end{array}$$ $$\begin{array}{r} 1 \\ 1 \\ +5 \\ \hline \end{array}$$

$$\begin{array}{r} 1 \\ 2 \\ +2 \\ \hline \end{array}$$ $$\begin{array}{r} 3 \\ 2 \\ +4 \\ \hline \end{array}$$ $$\begin{array}{r} 6 \\ 2 \\ +2 \\ \hline \end{array}$$ $$\begin{array}{r} 1 \\ 4 \\ +2 \\ \hline \end{array}$$ $$\begin{array}{r} 3 \\ 3 \\ +4 \\ \hline \end{array}$$ $$\begin{array}{r} 2 \\ 5 \\ +2 \\ \hline \end{array}$$

$$\begin{array}{r} 2 \\ 1 \\ +3 \\ \hline \end{array}$$ $$\begin{array}{r} 2 \\ 2 \\ +4 \\ \hline \end{array}$$ $$\begin{array}{r} 3 \\ 3 \\ +3 \\ \hline \end{array}$$ $$\begin{array}{r} 7 \\ 1 \\ +2 \\ \hline \end{array}$$ $$\begin{array}{r} 5 \\ 0 \\ +4 \\ \hline \end{array}$$ $$\begin{array}{r} 8 \\ 1 \\ +1 \\ \hline \end{array}$$

Ahmed has 4 🚗. He has 2 🚙.

He has 3 🚗. How many cars in all?

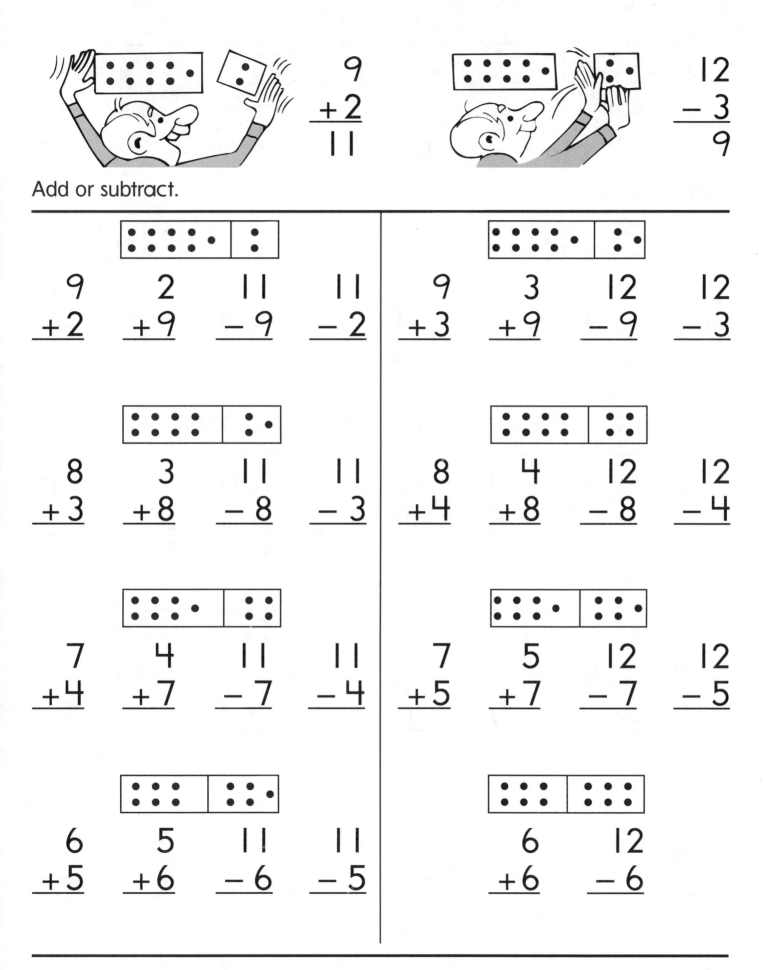

$$\begin{array}{r} 9 \\ +2 \\ \hline 11 \end{array}$$

$$\begin{array}{r} 12 \\ -3 \\ \hline 9 \end{array}$$

Add or subtract.

$$\begin{array}{r} 9 \\ +2 \\ \hline \end{array} \qquad \begin{array}{r} 2 \\ +9 \\ \hline \end{array} \qquad \begin{array}{r} 11 \\ -9 \\ \hline \end{array} \qquad \begin{array}{r} 11 \\ -2 \\ \hline \end{array} \qquad \begin{array}{r} 9 \\ +3 \\ \hline \end{array} \qquad \begin{array}{r} 3 \\ +9 \\ \hline \end{array} \qquad \begin{array}{r} 12 \\ -9 \\ \hline \end{array} \qquad \begin{array}{r} 12 \\ -3 \\ \hline \end{array}$$

$$\begin{array}{r} 8 \\ +3 \\ \hline \end{array} \qquad \begin{array}{r} 3 \\ +8 \\ \hline \end{array} \qquad \begin{array}{r} 11 \\ -8 \\ \hline \end{array} \qquad \begin{array}{r} 11 \\ -3 \\ \hline \end{array} \qquad \begin{array}{r} 8 \\ +4 \\ \hline \end{array} \qquad \begin{array}{r} 4 \\ +8 \\ \hline \end{array} \qquad \begin{array}{r} 12 \\ -8 \\ \hline \end{array} \qquad \begin{array}{r} 12 \\ -4 \\ \hline \end{array}$$

$$\begin{array}{r} 7 \\ +4 \\ \hline \end{array} \qquad \begin{array}{r} 4 \\ +7 \\ \hline \end{array} \qquad \begin{array}{r} 11 \\ -7 \\ \hline \end{array} \qquad \begin{array}{r} 11 \\ -4 \\ \hline \end{array} \qquad \begin{array}{r} 7 \\ +5 \\ \hline \end{array} \qquad \begin{array}{r} 5 \\ +7 \\ \hline \end{array} \qquad \begin{array}{r} 12 \\ -7 \\ \hline \end{array} \qquad \begin{array}{r} 12 \\ -5 \\ \hline \end{array}$$

$$\begin{array}{r} 6 \\ +5 \\ \hline \end{array} \qquad \begin{array}{r} 5 \\ +6 \\ \hline \end{array} \qquad \begin{array}{r} 11 \\ -6 \\ \hline \end{array} \qquad \begin{array}{r} 11 \\ -5 \\ \hline \end{array} \qquad \begin{array}{r} 6 \\ +6 \\ \hline \end{array} \qquad \begin{array}{r} 12 \\ -6 \\ \hline \end{array}$$

$$\begin{array}{r} 9 \\ +4 \\ \hline 13 \end{array}$$

$$\begin{array}{r} 14 \\ -5 \\ \hline 9 \end{array}$$

Add or subtract.

| $\begin{array}{r} 9 \\ +4 \end{array}$ | $\begin{array}{r} 4 \\ +9 \end{array}$ | $\begin{array}{r} 13 \\ -9 \end{array}$ | $\begin{array}{r} 13 \\ -4 \end{array}$ | $\begin{array}{r} 9 \\ +5 \end{array}$ | $\begin{array}{r} 5 \\ +9 \end{array}$ | $\begin{array}{r} 14 \\ -9 \end{array}$ | $\begin{array}{r} 14 \\ -5 \end{array}$ |

| $\begin{array}{r} 8 \\ +5 \end{array}$ | $\begin{array}{r} 5 \\ +8 \end{array}$ | $\begin{array}{r} 13 \\ -8 \end{array}$ | $\begin{array}{r} 13 \\ -5 \end{array}$ | $\begin{array}{r} 8 \\ +6 \end{array}$ | $\begin{array}{r} 6 \\ +8 \end{array}$ | $\begin{array}{r} 14 \\ -8 \end{array}$ | $\begin{array}{r} 14 \\ -6 \end{array}$ |

| $\begin{array}{r} 7 \\ +6 \end{array}$ | $\begin{array}{r} 6 \\ +7 \end{array}$ | $\begin{array}{r} 13 \\ -7 \end{array}$ | $\begin{array}{r} 13 \\ -6 \end{array}$ | $\begin{array}{r} 7 \\ +7 \end{array}$ | $\begin{array}{r} 14 \\ -7 \end{array}$ |

| $\begin{array}{r} 12 \\ -4 \end{array}$ | $\begin{array}{r} 8 \\ +6 \end{array}$ | $\begin{array}{r} 2 \\ +9 \end{array}$ | $\begin{array}{r} 14 \\ -8 \end{array}$ | $\begin{array}{r} 13 \\ -5 \end{array}$ | $\begin{array}{r} 7 \\ +6 \end{array}$ |

Addition and Subtraction: Facts for 13 and 14

Add or subtract.

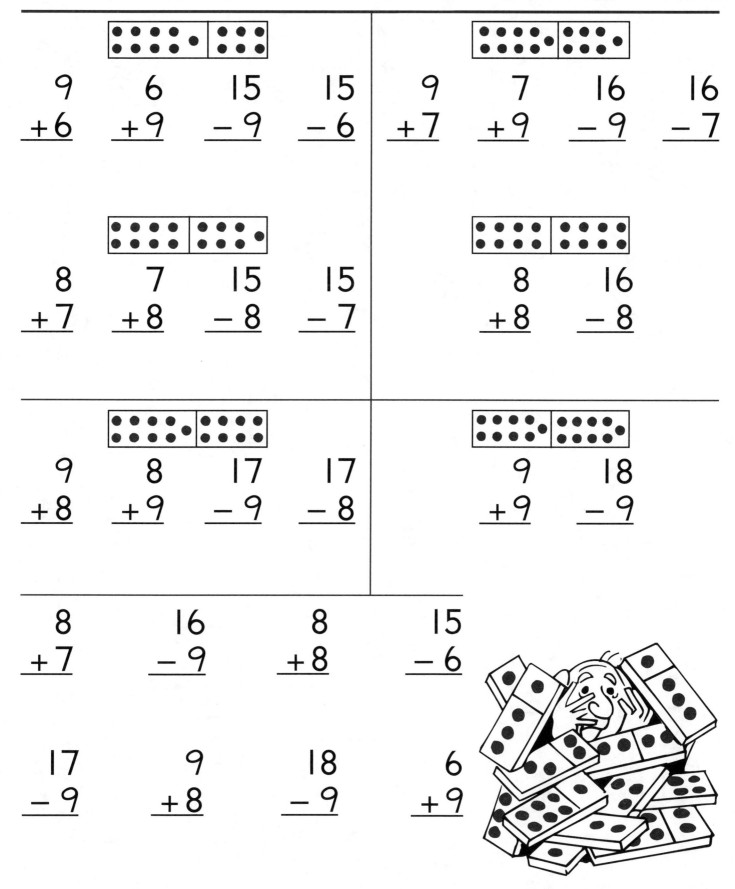

9	6	15	15
+6	+9	−9	−6

9	7	16	16
+7	+9	−9	−7

8	7	15	15
+7	+8	−8	−7

8	16
+8	−8

9	8	17	17
+8	+9	−9	−8

9	18
+9	−9

8	16	8	15
+7	−9	+8	−6

17	9	18	6
−9	+8	−9	+9

Match the mice with the cheese.

$$
\begin{array}{r} 8 \\ +4 \\ \hline \end{array}
\qquad
\begin{array}{r} 6 \\ +9 \\ \hline \end{array}
\qquad
\begin{array}{r} 3 \\ +8 \\ \hline \end{array}
$$

$$
\begin{array}{r} 7 \\ +4 \\ \hline \end{array}
\qquad\qquad
\begin{array}{r} 9 \\ +8 \\ \hline \end{array}
$$

$$
\begin{array}{r} 8 \\ +7 \\ \hline \end{array}
$$

$$
\begin{array}{r} 8 \\ +8 \\ \hline \end{array}
$$

$$
\begin{array}{r} 2 \\ +9 \\ \hline \end{array}
\qquad
\begin{array}{r} 6 \\ +6 \\ \hline \end{array}
\qquad
\begin{array}{r} 9 \\ +9 \\ \hline \end{array}
$$

$$
\begin{array}{r} 5 \\ +7 \\ \hline \end{array}
\qquad
\begin{array}{r} 6 \\ +8 \\ \hline \end{array}
$$

$$
\begin{array}{r} 8 \\ +5 \\ \hline \end{array}
\qquad\qquad
\begin{array}{r} 7 \\ +9 \\ \hline \end{array}
$$

$$
\begin{array}{r} 7 \\ +7 \\ \hline \end{array}
\qquad
\begin{array}{r} 6 \\ +7 \\ \hline \end{array}
$$

Mice: 11, 12, 13, 14, 15, 16, 17, 18

Addition Practice: Facts for 11–18

Circle the correct subtraction problem or problems in each row.

11 – 9　　13 – 8　　13 – 9　　12 – 8

11 – 7　　12 – 9　　11 – 8　　14 – 9

12 – 8　　13 – 9　　12 – 9　　11 – 7

14 – 8　　12 – 7　　13 – 6　　11 – 6

13 – 7　　11 – 4　　12 – 5　　15 – 9

15 – 8　　13 – 4　　14 – 7　　16 – 9

13 – 5　　16 – 8　　17 – 9　　14 – 6

11 – 2　　18 – 9　　12 – 6　　16 – 7

Subtraction Practice: Facts for 11–18

Step 1. Read
Step 2. Think—Add or subtract?
Step 3. Solve
Step 4. Check

There are 12 .

Then 5 .

How many now?

$$\begin{array}{r} 1\,2 \\ -\ 5 \\ \hline \end{array}$$

Bonnie makes 9 .

Then she makes 6 more.

How many now?

There are 14 .

Then 9 break.

How many are left?

Fatima makes 7 home runs.

Steve makes 6 home runs.

How many home runs in all?

---

11 are in a box.

Lisa takes out 3 .

How many now?

Problem Solving: Addition and Subtraction

Add.

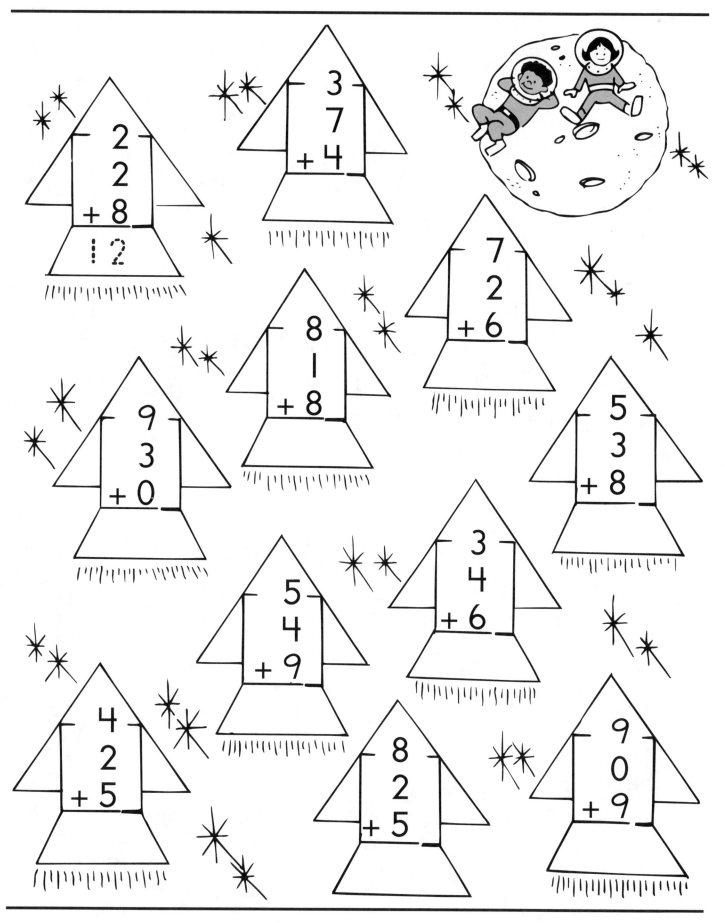

$$\begin{array}{r} 2 \\ 2 \\ +\ 8 \\ \hline 1\ 2 \end{array}$$

$$\begin{array}{r} 3 \\ 7 \\ +\ 4 \\ \hline \end{array}$$

$$\begin{array}{r} 7 \\ 2 \\ +\ 6 \\ \hline \end{array}$$

$$\begin{array}{r} 8 \\ 1 \\ +\ 8 \\ \hline \end{array}$$

$$\begin{array}{r} 9 \\ 3 \\ +\ 0 \\ \hline \end{array}$$

$$\begin{array}{r} 5 \\ 3 \\ +\ 8 \\ \hline \end{array}$$

$$\begin{array}{r} 5 \\ 4 \\ +\ 9 \\ \hline \end{array}$$

$$\begin{array}{r} 3 \\ 4 \\ +\ 6 \\ \hline \end{array}$$

$$\begin{array}{r} 4 \\ 2 \\ +\ 5 \\ \hline \end{array}$$

$$\begin{array}{r} 8 \\ 2 \\ +\ 5 \\ \hline \end{array}$$

$$\begin{array}{r} 9 \\ 0 \\ +\ 9 \\ \hline \end{array}$$

Three Addends: Sums to 18

Use the number line to add and subtract.

0 1 2 3 4 5 6 7 8 9 10 11 12 13 14 15 16 17 18 19 20

14 − 7 + 5 − 8 + 4 − 1 =

18 − 9 − 3 + 4 − 6 + 8 =

2 + 3 + 5 − 10 + 9 + 6 =

3 + 4 + 6 − 6 + 2 − 2 + 3 =

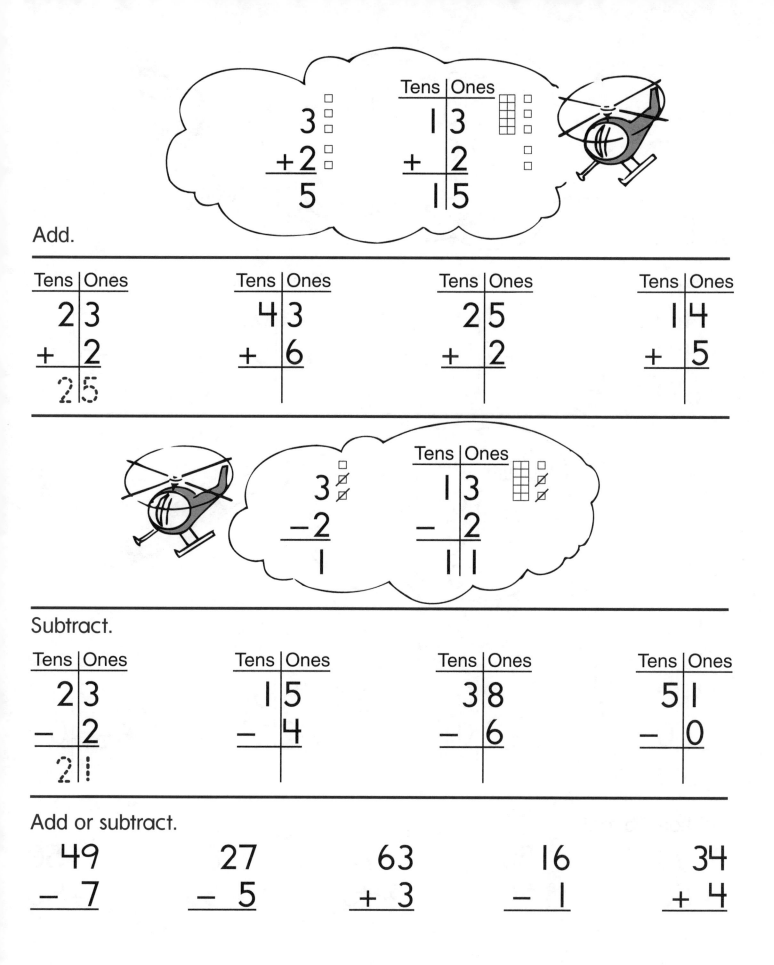

Example (top cloud):

Tens	Ones
	3
+	2
	5

Tens	Ones
1	3
+	2
1	5

Add.

Tens	Ones
2	3
+	2
2	5

Tens	Ones
4	3
+	6

Tens	Ones
2	5
+	2

Tens	Ones
1	4
+	5

Example (second cloud):

	Tens	Ones
	3	3
	−	2
		1

Tens	Ones
1	3
−	2
1	1

Subtract.

Tens	Ones
2	3
−	2
2	1

Tens	Ones
1	5
−	4

Tens	Ones
3	8
−	6

Tens	Ones
5	1
−	0

Add or subtract.

$$\begin{array}{r} 49 \\ -\ 7 \\ \hline \end{array} \qquad \begin{array}{r} 27 \\ -\ 5 \\ \hline \end{array} \qquad \begin{array}{r} 63 \\ +\ 3 \\ \hline \end{array} \qquad \begin{array}{r} 16 \\ -\ 1 \\ \hline \end{array} \qquad \begin{array}{r} 34 \\ +\ 4 \\ \hline \end{array}$$

Two-Digit Numbers: Adding and Subtracting Ones

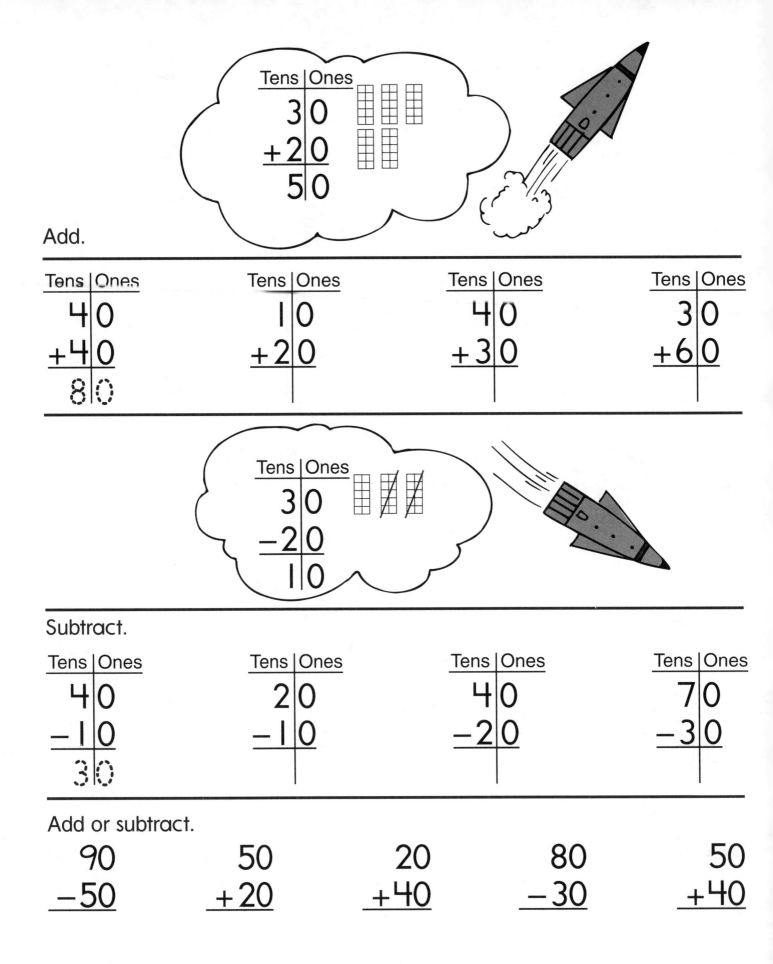

Tens	Ones
3	0
+2	0
5	0

Add.

Tens	Ones
4	0
+4	0
8	0

Tens	Ones
1	0
+2	0

Tens	Ones
4	0
+3	0

Tens	Ones
3	0
+6	0

Tens	Ones
3	0
-2	0
1	0

Subtract.

Tens	Ones
4	0
-1	0
3	0

Tens	Ones
2	0
-1	0

Tens	Ones
4	0
-2	0

Tens	Ones
7	0
-3	0

Add or subtract.

$$\begin{array}{r} 90 \\ -50 \\ \hline \end{array} \qquad \begin{array}{r} 50 \\ +20 \\ \hline \end{array} \qquad \begin{array}{r} 20 \\ +40 \\ \hline \end{array} \qquad \begin{array}{r} 80 \\ -30 \\ \hline \end{array} \qquad \begin{array}{r} 50 \\ +40 \\ \hline \end{array}$$

Two-Digit Numbers: Adding and Subtracting Tens

Add.

Tens	Ones
2	5
+3	2
5	7

Tens	Ones
1	6
+2	3
3	9

Tens	Ones
1	1
+3	5

Tens	Ones
2	4
+2	0

Tens	Ones
3	6
+2	2

Tens	Ones
4	4
+3	5

Tens	Ones
2	4
+2	4

Tens	Ones
3	2
+3	1

$$25$$
$$+53$$

$$24$$
$$+41$$

$$83$$
$$+15$$

$$30$$
$$+69$$

$$45$$
$$+24$$

$$65$$
$$+12$$

$$22$$
$$+67$$

$$31$$
$$+46$$

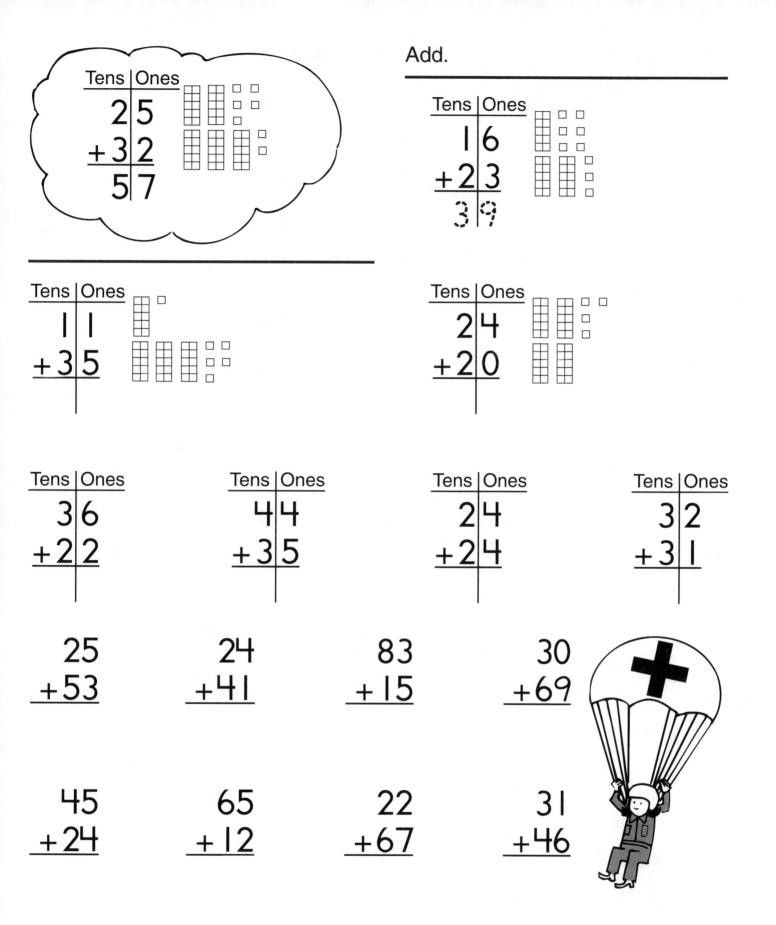

Adding Two-Digit Numbers

Tens	Ones
3	7
−2	3
1	4

Tens	Ones
2	4
−1	3

Tens	Ones
3	5
−1	2

Tens	Ones
2	9
−1	7

Tens	Ones
3	9
−2	5

Tens	Ones
7	8
−6	2

Tens	Ones
9	4
−4	2

Tens	Ones
6	7
−4	4

$$49 - 42$$ $$68 - 26$$ $$85 - 53$$ $$46 - 15$$

$$79 - 53$$ $$91 - 61$$ $$84 - 30$$ $$26 - 26$$

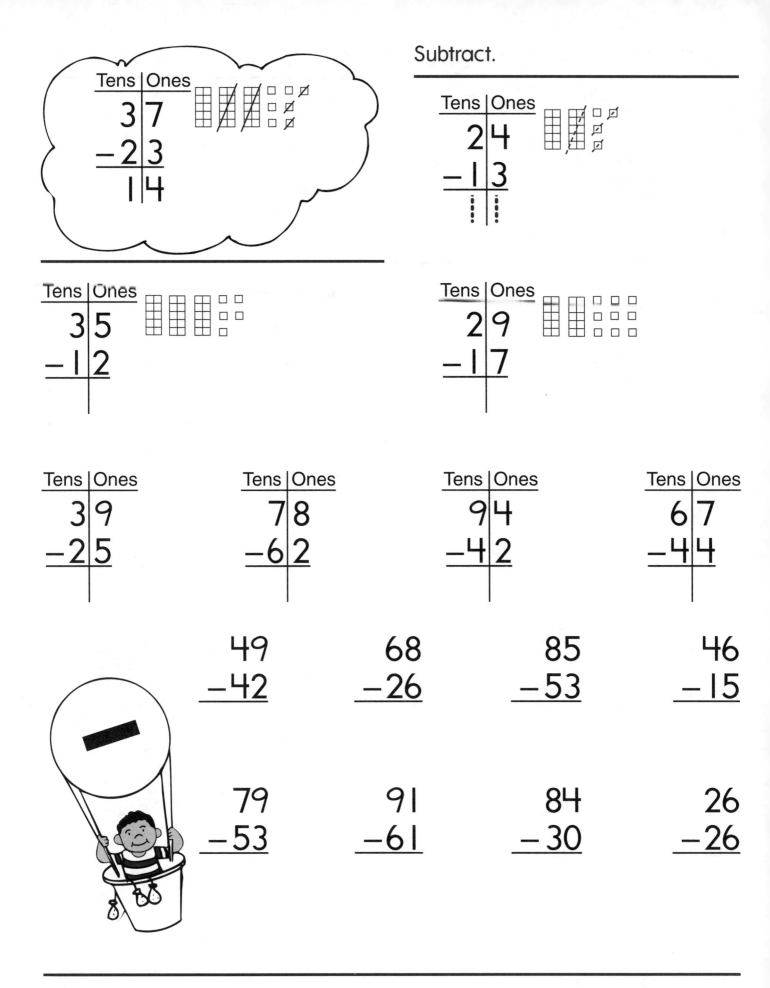

Subtracting Two-Digit Numbers

Add or subtract.

56 +42	67 −34	13 +25	

42 + 2	78 −55	96 −74

65 −53	80 −40	34 +34	28 +41	55 − 2

19 +60	43 +24	71 −30	25 +51	90 −80

Add.

5 3 +1	7 2 +8	4 6 +4	8 3 +4	2 3 +5	9 3 +6

Read, think, solve, and check. Mark the problem you cannot do.

16 🐎 go up and down.

13 🐎 do not.

How many 🐎 in all?

$$\begin{array}{r} 16 \\ +13 \\ \hline \end{array}$$

👨 has 69 🍬.

He sells 53 🍬.

How many 🍬 are left?

Many children are on

the ☸ .

12 more children get on.

How many children now?

Gigi gets 3 🎈.

Binh gets 6 🎈.

Jennie gets 4 🎈.

How many 🎈 in all?

58 🍿 are in the box.

John eats 44 🍿.

How many 🍿 now?

Problem Solving: Insufficient Information

SNACKS

Find how many cents are in all.

Kam has 75¢. How much will be left if she buys —

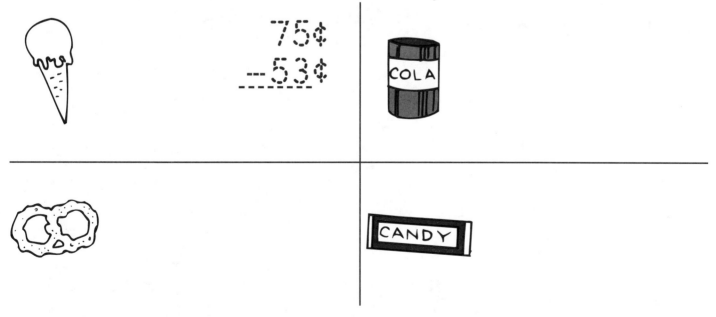

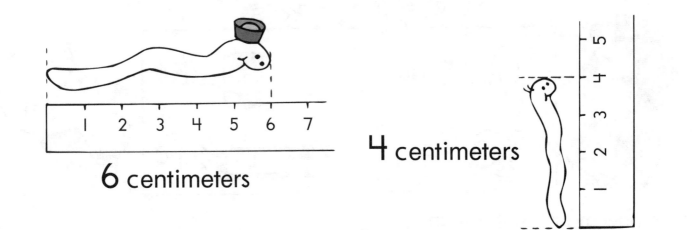

6 centimeters

4 centimeters

Measure each worm with a centimeter ruler.

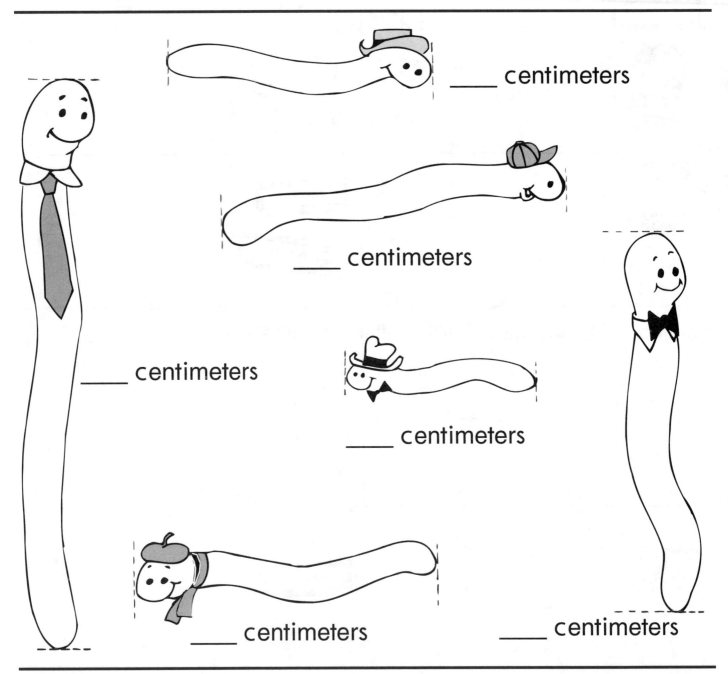

____ centimeters

____ centimeters

____ centimeters

____ centimeters

____ centimeters

____ centimeters

____ centimeters

Measurement: Centimeter

Map of Henry's Neighborhood

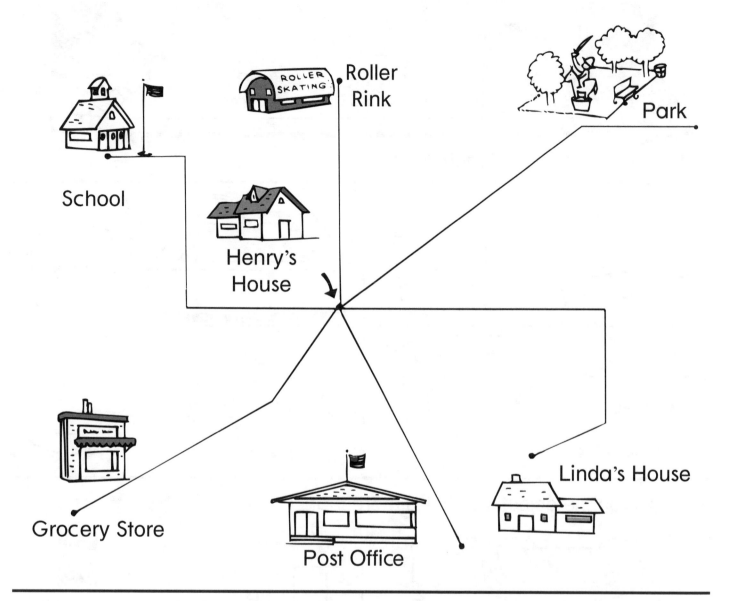

Measure each line on the map with a centimeter ruler.

Find the distance from Henry's house to —

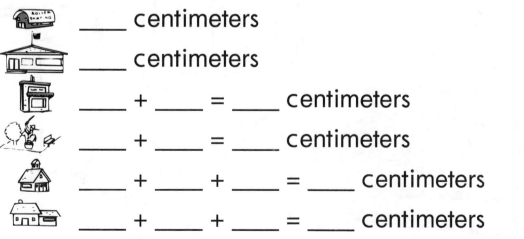

_____ centimeters

_____ centimeters

_____ + _____ = _____ centimeters

_____ + _____ = _____ centimeters

_____ + _____ + _____ = _____ centimeters

_____ + _____ + _____ = _____ centimeters

Measurement: Centimeter

Put an X on the object that holds **more.**

liter

liter

liter

liter

Put an X on the object that holds more than 1 liter.

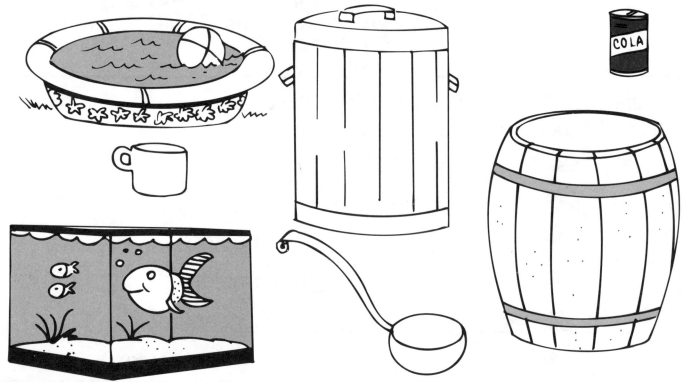

COLA

Measurement: Liter

 Two loaves of bread weigh about 1 kilogram.

Put an X on each object that weighs more than 1 kilogram.

Circle each object that weighs less than 1 kilogram.

Measurement: Kilogram

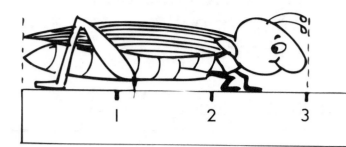

3 inches

2 inches

Measure each bug with an inch ruler.

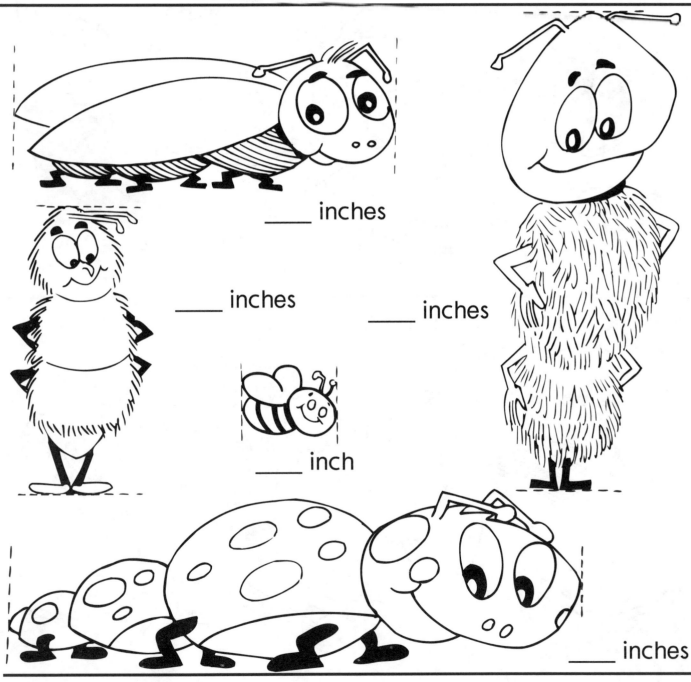

_____ inches

_____ inches

_____ inches

_____ inch

_____ inches

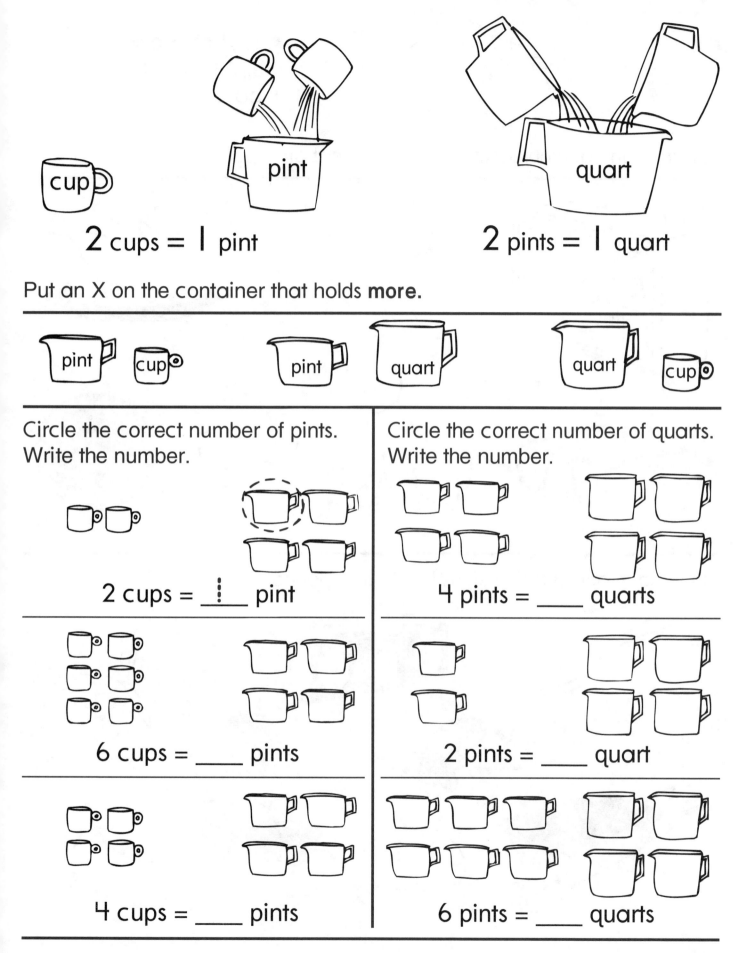

cup

pint

quart

2 cups = **1** pint

2 pints = **1** quart

Put an X on the container that holds **more.**

pint   cup   pint   quart   quart   cup

Circle the correct number of pints.
Write the number.

2 cups = ___ pint

6 cups = ___ pints

4 cups = ___ pints

Circle the correct number of quarts.
Write the number.

4 pints = ___ quarts

2 pints = ___ quart

6 pints = ___ quarts

A loaf of bread
weighs about
1 pound.

Put an X on each object that weighs more than 1 pound.

Circle each object that weighs less than 1 pound.

Measurement: Pound